Statistical Reasoning

Lloyd Rosenberg

The Bernard M. Baruch College
of
The City University of New York

Statistical Reasoning

Charles E. Merrill Publishing Company
Columbus, Ohio
A Bell & Howell Company

Merrill's
Mathematics and
Quantitative Methods
Series

under the editorship of
Vincent E. Cangelosi
and
Melvin J. Hinich

International Standard Book Number: 0-675-09329-5 (cloth)
0-675-09330-9 (paper)

Library of Congress Catalog Card Number: 76-117378
Printed in the United States of America
1 2 3 4 5 6 7 8 — 75 74 73 72 71 70

To T.R. and M.R.

Editors' Preface

This series is a new approach to the ever-growing problem of providing appropriate material for basic mathematics courses offered for those planning careers in fields other than mathematics. Rapidly changing concepts in what should be offered at the undergraduate level have led to many approaches with various arrangements of topics. A serious problem arises in an effort to implement all of the material needed to satisfy the needs of these different courses. Too often there is no single book that treats the material in the desired manner or includes the desired topics at an acceptable level.

This series is planned as an integrated group of high quality books, each complete within itself except for required background material, each covering a specified topic, and each preparing the reader for the topics that would follow naturally.

With the flexibility that such a series offers, it is hoped that every requirement can be satisfied by a careful selection of books. In designing the series, we have tried to meet two requirements. We have tried, first, to satisfy the need for flexibility in the subject material; and secondly, to present to the reader material that has been prepared by an author with a specialized background in that particular area.

In editing this series, we have insisted that each author treat the subject material in a way to give it operational meaning. With the specialist's greater familiarity in a particular subject, he can delicately merge the abstract with the practical. He can give a functional interpretation to the concepts of mathematics, thereby motivating the student and creating the necessary interest to make the learning experience exciting.

We owe a deep debt of gratitude to each author who has contributed to the series. Further, we are grateful to Charles E. Merrill Publishing

Company for the assistance they have given us in the development of this series.

Baton Rouge, Louisiana   Vincent E. Cangelosi
Pittsburgh, Pennsylvania   Melvin J. Hinich

Author's Preface

The major aim of this text is to present the fundamental concepts of modern statistics. It is not intended as a book of statistical methods and, because of length limitations, many important problems are not discussed. It is the author's hope that this book will give the reader an understanding of how statistical procedures are developed and evaluated, so that he may more critically evaluate those procedures which he encounters.

The prerequisites for understanding this text are a knowledge of probability theory, differential calculus, and integral calculus equivalent to the material contained in four titles in the Merrill Mathematics and Quantitative Methods Series: *Introduction to Finite Probability, Continuous Probability Theory, Differential Calculus* and *Integral Calculus*. The material in this book, together with material on probability theory, has been used by the author in a one-semester course in the foundations of statistics. An interested reader with proper prerequisites should be able to follow the material without difficulty. The reader who wishes to avoid some of the mathematical details may omit Sections 2-3, 2-5, 3-3 and 3-5 without destroying the continuity of the exposition.

The author would like to thank Professor Melvin Hinich for his invitation to participate in the Merrill Mathematics and Quantitative Methods Series. The comments, or lack of them, from students who were exposed to a preliminary version of this manuscript have also been greatly appreciated. Finally I would like to thank Florence DiDonato and Bea Stuhmer for typing parts of the preliminary version of the manuscript, and Mary Jane Everett for typing the final manuscript.

Lloyd Rosenberg

Contents

Statistical Reasoning

chapter one

Basic Concepts

1-1. INTRODUCTION

Problem 1-1-1. A distributor of household appliances has just decided to distribute electric ranges. He realizes that the weekly demand for these ranges, X, will not be constant but will vary from week to week. From his previous experience with similar appliances he is able to assume that

$$P[X = j] = \frac{\lambda^j e^{-\lambda}}{j!} \qquad j = 0, 1, 2, \ldots \qquad (1\text{-}1\text{-}1)$$

where $\lambda > 0$ is the mean number of ranges demanded per week. The distributor would like to have some idea of the number of orders he can reasonably expect per week in order to determine the size of his inventory. This would be possible if he knew the true value of λ. The problem of determining the value of λ by observing the number of ranges demanded over several weeks is called a *problem of estimation*.

Problem 1-1-2. A manufacturer of electronic equipment wishes to determine if he should change from the type of transistor he presently uses to a different type. The only criterion on which the decision will be based is whether the mean length of life of the new type of transistor is greater than that of the type presently used. Since different transistors will last different lengths of time, each type is tested to determine its length of life. Assume that the lengths of life of the new type and the old type of transistor are normally distributed with means μ_N and μ_0, respectively, and that each has variance one. On the basis of these experiments, the manufacturer will decide if the new type of transistor has a longer mean life than the old type. This is a *problem of hypothesis testing*.

Problem 1-1-3. An advertising agency wishes to determine what proportion (p) of people who subscribe to *Life* magazine also subscribe to *Time* magazine. They might do this by checking every subscriber who subscribes to *Life* against the list of subscribers to *Time*. But that would be time-consuming, so an alternative method is proposed: Select *at random* 100 people from the list of subscribers to *Life*. By choosing *at random* we will mean that each subscriber has an equal probability of being selected each time; *i.e.*, if there were 100,000 subscribers, each would have 1/100,000 chance of being selected at each selection.* Then, if we check our sample of 100 to find what proportion of it is constituted by subscribers to *Time*, we can use that proportion as an estimate of p. This problem also is one of estimation.

The first common element in each of these problems is that there is a probabilistic model to describe the outcomes of the various observations or experiments. In Problems 1-1-1 and 1-1-2 the probabilistic model is inherent in the nature of the problems, that is, the demands will vary from week to week and the length of life will vary from transistor to transistor. In Problem 1-1-3, however, the probabilistic model is introduced by the investigator through his sampling method. If the first 100 names of an alphabetical list of subscribers were selected, there would be no probabilistic model. But in the given procedure, there is a probability p that any person in the sample will also be a subscriber to *Time*.

The second common element in these examples is that the probabilistic model is not completely specified. In Problem 1-1-1 we do not know λ, in Problem 1-1-2 we do not know μ_N and μ_0, and in Problem 1-1-3 we do not know p. To make some inference about a partially specified model we take observations. We do not always wish to use these observations to make the same type of inference about each model. In Problems 1-1-1 and 1-1-3 we wish to determine the values of λ and p, respectively, whereas

---

*This definition allows the same person to appear in the sample more than once. The more rigorous definition of selecting a sample at random in this case would be that each possible sample of size 100 has an equal probability of being selected.

in Problem 1-1-2 actual values are not important, but we wish to determine whether $\mu_N > \mu_0$. Thus we arrive at our first definition.

Definition 1-1-1. Statistical reasoning is concerned with the use of observations taken at random to make inferences about phenomena whose outcomes are described by a partially specified probabilistic model.

Since probabilistic models are at the heart of statistical reasoning the remainder of this chapter will be devoted to some general concepts of probability models which are used in statistics.

1-2. POPULATION

In Problem 1-1-3 the group of people with which we are concerned consists of the 100,000 subscribers to *Life* magazine. This *population* is an existing group of people about whom we are trying to make some inference, *i.e.*, the proportion of *Life* subscribers who also receive *Time*. In Problem 1-1-1 there does not exist a real collection of elements under consideration but rather a conceptual collection. We have assumed that the number of orders per week is a Poisson-distributed random variable with parameter λ. If an urn consists of a very large number of slips of paper numbered 0, 1, 2, 3, ..., where slips having any number are in such proportion as to be approximately equal to the Poisson probabilities given by (1-1-1), then these slips may be considered as the fictitious population about which we will make our inference. They would correspond to the outcome of weekly demands if we could observe the phenomena for an indefinite length of time under identical conditions. We are then led to:

Definition 1-2-1. A *population* is a collection of elements real or fictitious having different characteristics for a particular attribute * about which an inference is to be made. The characteristics are so defined that they may be given by numerical values.

Definition 1-2-2. The characteristics of N elements of the population denoted by $X_1, X_2, \ldots, X_N$ are said to be a *random sample of N observations* from a given population if they are independent, identically distributed** random variables having a common distribution function. This

---

*We will not consider simultaneously the characteristics of more than one attribute in any particular discussion.

**The identical distribution of each observation will not apply to sampling from a finite population without replacement, but we will not consider this type of sampling problem.

distribution function will assign probabilities in such a way that the probability of selecting an individual having a characteristic less than or equal to the real number b corresponds to the proportion of elements in the population having a characteristic less than or equal to the real number b.

In Problems 1-1-1 and 1-1-3 the attributes being considered are the demand for ranges and the readership of *Time* magazine, respectively; the characteristics of these attributes are the number demanded, and 0 to 1, denoting the non-readership or readership of *Time* magazine. These characteristics can be described by integer values and the corresponding random variables are discrete random variables. In Problem 1-1-2 the attribute under consideration is the life of a transistor. Its characteristic, not necessarily represented in terms of integer values, is the length of life. So in order to include both the discrete and continuous cases in one definition, we have posed the definition of random sample in terms of the probabilities of the characteristics being less than or equal to a particular value.

The structure of the fictitious or real populations is determined by the probabilistic models assumed, and this determines the proportion of elements with a given characteristic occurring in any interval. We can now give an alternative definition of statistical reasoning.

Definition 1-2-3. Statistical reasoning is concerned with the use of a random sample of observations from one or several given populations to make inferences about certain unspecified properties of these populations.

1–3. LIKELIHOOD FUNCTION

In Problem 1-1-1, assume that we will observe the number of electric ranges demanded for four weeks. We will denote the weekly amounts by X_1, X_2, X_3, X_4, where each is a random variable having a Poisson distribution with parameter λ. If we assume, in addition, that the X_i are mutually independent, then we say that the X_i are a *random sample* of size 4 from a population having a Poisson distribution with parameter λ. We can compute the probability of the sample values being j_1, j_2, j_3, and j_4 respectively as:

$$P[X_1 = j_1, X_2 = j_2, X_3 = j_3, X_4 = j_4]$$

$$= \prod_{i=1}^{4} P[X_i = j_i] = \frac{\lambda^{\sum_{i=1}^{4} j_i} e^{-4\lambda}}{j_1! \, j_2! \, j_3! \, j_4!} = p(j_1, j_2, j_3, j_4, \lambda) \quad (1\text{-}3\text{-}1)$$

for all possible values of j_1, j_2, j_3, and j_4. We denote the expression given in (1-3-1) by $p(j_1, j_2, j_3, j_4, \lambda)$ since in order to compute any numerical value of this probability all five quantities must be known. If after observing the number of electric ranges demanded for each of four weeks we find that $X_1 = 4$, $X_2 = 3$, $X_3 = 2$, and $X_4 = 4$, that is $j_1 = 4$, $j_2 = 3$, $j_3 = 2$, and $j_4 = 4$, we then can compute the probability of observing these values from (1-3-1) as

$$P[X_1 = 4, X_2 = 3, X_3 = 2, X_4 = 4] = \frac{\lambda^{13} e^{-4\lambda}}{4! \, 3! \, 2! \, 4!} \qquad (1\text{-}3\text{-}2)$$

Now this probability only depends upon the unspecified parameter λ since we are considering fixed values of j_1, j_2, j_3, and j_4. The expression on the right of (1-3-2) or the expression on the right of (1-3-1) when considered only as a function λ with j_1, j_2, j_3, and j_4 fixed is called the *likelihood function*.

In Problem 1-1-3, our observation consists of determining whether or not a person selected at random is a reader of *Time*. We will say that the random variable $X_i = 1$ if person i in the sample reads *Time*, whereas $X_i = 0$ if this person does not. From the method in which the sample is selected we have: $P[X_i = 1] = p$; $P[X_i = 0] = 1 - p = q$ $i = 1, 2, \ldots,$ 100, and $X_1, X_2, \ldots, X_{100}$ are mutually independent random variables. We can now compute the probability of any arbitrary sample values $j_1, j_2, \ldots, j_{100}$ as

$$P[X_1 = j_1, X_2 = j_2, \ldots, X_{100} = j_{100}]$$

$$= \prod_{i=1}^{100} P[X_i = j_i] = p^{\sum\limits_{i=1}^{100} j_i} (1 - p)^{100 - \sum\limits_{i=1}^{100} j_i} \qquad 0 \leq p \leq 1 \qquad (1\text{-}3\text{-}3)$$

where the j_i can assume all possible combinations of 0's and 1's. Because the values of j_i can only be 0 or 1 $\sum_{i=1}^{100} j_i$ gives the number of people in the sample who read *Time* and $100 - \sum_{i=1}^{100} j_i$ are the number of people who do not, which accounts for (1-3-3). If we consider (1-3-3) as a function of the unknown parameter p then it is again a *likelihood function*.

We will now give a more precise definition of the concept of likelihood function when the random variables $X_1, X_2, \ldots, X_N$ are discrete. Let us assume that $x_1, x_2, \ldots, x_N$ are particular outcomes of a random sample of N observations and that $p(x, \theta_1, \theta_2, \ldots, \theta_m)^*$ is the probability of observing the characteristic value x where $\theta_1, \theta_2, \ldots, \theta_m$ are m unspecified parameters. The probability of the particular outcome of the random sample is given by $\prod_{i=1}^{N} p(x_i, \theta_1, \theta_2, \ldots, \theta_m)$ since each random variable is independent and identically distributed. If we take $m = 1$, $\theta = \lambda$, and $x = j$ then we have the probability mass function of the form defined in (1-1-1).

---

*Since we will only consider one attribute in any discussion we need not consider any multivariate density function or mass function.

Definition 1-3-1. If we consider the probability of the outcome of a particular random sample $x_1, x_2, \ldots, x_N$ as a function of the unknown parameters $\theta_1, \theta_2, \ldots, \theta_m$ this function is called the *likelihood function*, that is,*

$$\prod_{i=1}^{N} p(x_i, \theta_1, \theta_2, \ldots, \theta_m) = g(\theta_1, \theta_2, \ldots, \theta_m)$$

We also must specify some condition on the parameters $\theta_1, \theta_2, \ldots, \theta_m$ in order to completely specify the likelihood function. In the likelihood function of (1-3-2), $\lambda > 0$; in the likelihood function of (1-3-1), $0 \leq p \leq 1$. These conditions will be specified explicitly for particular likelihood functions, but for the general case we will say that $(\theta_1, \theta_2, \ldots, \theta_m)$ belongs to an arbitrary set which will sometimes be referred to as the *parameter space*. The parameter space for the likelihood function of (1-3-1) is all positive numbers and for (1-3-3) all numbers 0 through 1.

We will now consider the case where the characteristics of the attribute of the elements in the population is such that it is described by a continuous random variable. In Problem 1-1-2 the attribute is the life of a type of transistor and the characteristic is the length of the life.** If we consider the length of life of a new transistor to have the density function

$$f(x, \mu_N) = \frac{1}{\sqrt{2\pi}} \exp -\frac{1}{2}(x - \mu_N)^2 \qquad \begin{array}{l} -\infty < x < \infty \\ -\infty < \mu_N < \infty \end{array}$$

then the joint density function associated with a particular random sample of observations $x_1, x_2, \ldots, x_N$ is given by

$$\prod_{i=1}^{N} f(x_i, \mu_N) = \left(\frac{1}{\sqrt{2\pi}}\right)^N e^{-1/2 \sum_{i=1}^{N} (x_i - \mu_N)^2}$$
$$= g(\mu_N) \qquad -\infty < \mu_N < \infty \qquad (1\text{-}3\text{-}5)$$

Considering this joint density function as a function of the unknown parameter μ_N, which we denote by $g(\mu_N)$, it is again called the *likelihood function*.

In general, assuming that $x_1, x_2, \ldots, x_N$ are particular outcomes of a random sample of N observations and that $f(x_i, \theta_1, \theta_2, \ldots, \theta_m)$ is the density function associated with the characteristic value x_i, where $\theta_1, \theta_2, \ldots, \theta_m$ are m unspecified parameters, then we have:

Definition 1-3-2. If we consider the joint density function associated with the outcome of a particular random sample $x_1, x_2, \ldots, x_N$ as a function

---

*In most cases which we will consider, $m = 1$; therefore the likelihood function is a function of a single variable.

**For this same attribute we could have defined the characteristic to be 0 if the transistor lasts less than 10 hours, and 1 if it lasts at least 10 hours. Thus, for the same elements and attributes, different characteristics may lead to different conceptual populations about which we are trying to make inferences.

of the unknown parameters $\theta_1, \theta_2, \ldots, \theta_m$, this function is called the *likelihood function;* that is,

$$\prod_{i=1}^{N} f(x_i, \theta_1, \theta_2, \ldots, \theta_N) = g(\theta_1, \theta_2, \ldots, \theta_N)$$

is the likelihood function.

The comments about the parameter specifications, made after Definition 1-3-1, are also applicable here. The parameter space for the likelihood function of (1-3-5) consists of all real numbers.

1-4. SUFFICIENT STATISTICS

Although our stated intention is to make inferences about certain properties of populations from a random sample of observations, we must first consider the problem of summarizing these observations in a meaningful way. The summarization of information by the use of a few numbers was, for many years, the primary use of statistics. For example, accurate records of births and deaths have long been kept and this information is summarized in various forms such as the proportion of people in a particular age group who died. For our purposes, however, it will also be useful to summarize the information contained in our random sample as an intermediate step in making inferences. Any such summarization is called a statistic.

Definition 1-4-1. A *statistic* is any function of the random sample $X_1, X_2, \ldots, X_N$ which we will usually denote by $t(X_1, X_2, \ldots, X_N)$.*

If in Problem 1-1-3 we take a random sample $X_1, X_2, \ldots, X_N$, then one statistic we could define is $\bar{X} = (X_1 + X_2 + \ldots + X_N)/N$. Now we need to know if this statistic meaningfully summarizes the information contained in the sample. Suppose that the likelihood function will be the basis for our inferences concerning the unknown parameter p. For a random sample $x_1, x_2, \ldots, x_N$, we obtain, from (1-3-3),

$$g(p) = p^{\sum_{i=1}^{N} x_i}(1 - p)^{N - \sum_{i=1}^{N} x_i} \qquad 0 \leqq p \leqq 1 \qquad (1\text{-}4\text{-}1)$$

so that a knowledge of $\sum_{i=1}^{N} x_i = N\bar{x}$ is sufficient for the construction of the likelihood function.

---

*Random variables are denoted by upper case letters, and specific values of the random variables by lower case letters. Being a function of random variables, a statistic itself is a random variable.

If we consider Problem 1-1-1, we now have the likelihood function given by:

$$g(\lambda) = \frac{\lambda^{\sum\limits_{i=1}^{N} x_i} e^{-N\lambda}}{\prod\limits_{i=1}^{N} x_i!} \qquad \lambda > 0 \qquad (1\text{-}4\text{-}2)$$

A knowledge of the random vaiable $\bar{X}$ is no longer sufficient for the exact reconstruction of the likelihood function.

If all that is known is $\bar{x} = 7$ and $N = 3$, then the numerator of (1-4-2) can be constructed exactly but the denominator depends on the particular values x_1, x_2, and x_3 which are observed. But recall that we are only concerned with the likelihood function as a function λ so that we may reconstruct the likelihood function except for a multiplicative constant. In subsequent chapters we will see that this multiplicative factor, depending upon the specific values x_1, x_2, and x_3, will not affect our inferences concerning λ. Thus, we have

Definition 1-4-2.* A set of statistics $t_1(X_1, X_2, \ldots, X_N)$, $t_2(X_1, X_2, \ldots, X_N), \ldots, t_p(X_1, X_2, \ldots, X_N)$ is said to be sufficient for the density (probability mass) function $f(x, \theta_1, \theta_2, \ldots, \theta_m)$ $(p(x, \theta_1, \theta_2, \ldots, \theta_m))$ if, and only if, the likelihood function can be written in the form

$$\prod_{i=1}^{N} f(x_1, \theta_1, \theta_2, \ldots, \theta_m) \left(\prod_{i=1}^{N} p(x_1, \theta_1, \theta_2, \ldots, \theta_m) \right)$$
$$= h(x_1, x_2, \ldots, x_N) k(t_1, \ldots, t_p, \theta_1, \theta_2, \ldots, \theta_m)$$

where

$$h(x_1, x_2, \ldots, x_N) > 0$$

In the remainder of the book, we will not explicitly distinguish between the case where we have a probability mass function and a probability density function, but will always use the latter, since the definitions and results for both cases are the same.

From this definition we may now state that $t_1(X_1, X_2, \ldots, X_N) = \bar{X}$ is a sufficient statistic for the Poisson probability mass function since:

$$\prod_{i=1}^{N} p((x_i, \lambda) = \frac{1}{\prod\limits_{i=1}^{N} x_i!} \lambda^{N\bar{x}} e^{-N\lambda} \qquad (1\text{-}4\text{-}3)$$

---

*In more precise statements of this property there is an integrability condition placed upon the function $h(x_1, x_2, \ldots, x_N)$ but in all the examples we have considered this condition can be satisfied by multiplying and dividing by an appropriate function of the statistics which does not depend upon the parameters.

where

$$h(x_1, x_2, \ldots, x_N) = \frac{1}{\prod\limits_{i=1}^{N} \mathbf{x}_i!}$$

and

$$k(t_1, \lambda) = \lambda^{Nt_1} e^{-N\lambda}$$

We will now show that $t_1(x_1, x_2, \ldots, x_N) = \bar{x}$ and $t_2(x_1, x_2, \ldots, x_N) = \sum_{i=1}^{N} (x_i - \bar{x})^2$ are a sufficient set of statistics for the normal probability density function with mean μ and variance σ^2. This follows since

$$\prod_{i=1}^{N} f(x_i, \mu, \sigma^2) = \left(\frac{1}{\sqrt{2\pi}\,\sigma}\right)^N e^{-1/2\sigma^2 \left(\sum\limits_{i=1}^{N}(x_i-\mu)^2\right)}$$

$$= \left(\frac{1}{\sqrt{2\pi}\,\sigma}\right)^N e^{-1/2\sigma^2 \left(\sum\limits_{i=1}^{N}(x_i-\bar{x}+\bar{x}-\mu)^2\right)}$$

$$= \left(\frac{1}{\sqrt{2\pi}\,\sigma}\right)^N e^{-1\sqrt{2\pi}\,\sigma^2(t_2+(t_1-\mu)^2)}$$

which, taking $h(x_1, x_2, \ldots, x_N) = 1$ in Definition 1-4-2, shows that (t_1, t_2) is a sufficient set of statistics for the normal probability density function.

The definition of a sufficient set of statistics states that the joint probability density function or mass function can be factored into two parts; one depending only on the observations and the other depending only upon the statistics and the parameters. Clearly this is a very special property of the probability density function, or probability mass function, though fortunately many of those functions used in practical models have this property. The criterion we have used to define sufficient statistics is sometimes called the *Neyman criterion*. Since a knowledge of a sufficient set of statistics is enough to reproduce the likelihood function, except for the factor $h(x_1, x_2, \ldots, x_N)$ it is sometimes stated that sufficient statistics contain all the information contained in the sample.

There is come amount of indefiniteness in the number of statistics which make up a set of sufficient statistics. For example, if we define the statistics $t_1(X_1, X_2, \ldots, X_N) = X_1$, $t_2(X_1, X_2, \ldots, X_N) = X_2, \ldots,$ $t_N(X_1, X_2, \ldots, X_N) = X_N$, then from our definition we see that $(t_1, t_2, \ldots, t_N)$ form a sufficient set of statistics for the parameters $(\theta_1, \theta_2, \ldots, \theta_m)$. Our objective, then, concerning sufficient statistics, is to find not merely a set of sufficient statistics but one with as few statistics as possible, in order to obtain only the minimum of data needed to make inferences.

Exercises

1-1. With regard to the definition of a population, discuss the problems faced by a person taking a survey in September to predict the outcome of an election in November. Is there a difference between the population sampled from and the population about which the inference is to be made?

1-2. Define three attributes and their characteristics for the current freshman class.

1-3. Define an appropriate probabilistic model for the following problems. What are the unknown quantities and what inference is to be made about these quantities?
   (a) A freshman taking a mathematics course would like to know: What are his chances of receiving a grade of A? A passing grade?
   (b) A manufacturer of light bulbs would like to investigate the average length of life of his product. How often does it last more than 100 hours?
   (c) An advertising agency wishes to determine if their latest campaign has improved the sales of a product.

1-4. For the following probability mass functions, obtain the likelihood functions for a random sample of size N.

   (a) Binomial $x = 0, 1, 2, \ldots n$

   $$p(x, \theta) = \binom{n}{x} \theta^x (1 - \theta)^{n-x} \qquad 0 \leq \theta \leq 1$$

   (b) Geometric $x = 1, 2, \ldots$
   $$p(x, \theta) = \theta^{x-1}(1 - \theta) \qquad 0 \leq \theta \leq 1$$

1-5. For the probability mass functions in Exercise 1-4, is $\bar{X} = (X_1 + X_2 + \ldots + X_N)/N$ a sufficient statistic? Justify your answer.

1-6. For the following probability density functions obtain the likelihood functions for a sample of size N.

   (a) Exponential
   $$f(x, \theta) = \theta e^{-\theta x} \qquad X \geq 0 \qquad \theta > 0$$
   $$ = 0 \qquad \text{otherwise}$$

(b) Uniform

$f(x, \theta) = 1/\theta \quad 0 \leq x \leq \theta \quad \theta > 0$
$\quad\quad = 0 \quad$ otherwise

(c) Gamma

$f(x, \theta) = \dfrac{\theta}{(r-1)!} (\theta x)^{r-1} e^{-\theta x} \quad x \geq 0 \quad \theta > 0$
$\quad\quad = 0 \quad$ otherwise $\quad\quad r$ known

1-7. For the probability density function in Exercise 1–6, is $\bar{X} = (X_1 + X_2 + \ldots + X_N/N$ a sufficient statistic? Justify your answer.

chapter two

Point Estimation

2-1. INTRODUCTION

In Problem 1-1-1 we assume a probability model which is completely specified except for a parameter λ. We are to find the value of λ from observing the number of ranges purchased weekly in a period of several weeks. This is called a problem of *point estimation* because, from the set of values $\lambda > 0$ (the parameter space) which may be considered as all points greater than zero on a horizontal axis, we are to select one value; that is, one point. A similar problem of point estimation is posed in Problem 1-1-3 where we are asked to find a value of the parameter p, $0 \leqq p \leqq 1$.

Suppose that $X_1, X_2, \ldots, X_N$ is a random sample of N observations where each X_i has density function $f(x, \theta_1, \theta_2, \ldots, \theta_m)$. We then say:

Definition 2-1-1. A statistic $t_j(X_1, X_2, \ldots, X_N)$ whose value for a particular realization of the N observations is used as a *point estimate* of the parameter θ_j is called an *estimator* for θ_j.

In Problem 1-1-1 we can take $(X_1 + X_2 + \cdots + X_N)/N$ as an estimator for λ; for the particular realization $X_1 = 4$, $X_2 = 3$, $X_3 = 2$, $X_4 = 4$, an estimate of λ is 3.25.

2–2. PROPERTIES OF ESTIMATORS

We must now examine methods of constructing estimators and criteria for determining if a particular estimator is acceptable. Since an estimator is a random variable it will have a probability distribution associated with it. Thus, in Problem 1-1-2, if we choose $\bar{X}_N = (X_1 + X_2 + \cdots + X_N)/N$ as an estimator for μ_0, the moment generating function of $\bar{X}_N$ is given by

$$E(e^{t\bar{X}_N}) = E\left(\prod_{i=1}^{N} e^{tX_i/N}\right)$$
$$= \prod_{i=1}^{N} E(e^{tx_i/N})$$
$$= e^{t\mu_0 - t^2/2N^2}$$

Since this is the moment generating function of a normal random variable with mean μ_0 and variance $1/N$, we may state that this is the probability distribution of the estimator $\bar{X}_N$. We can find the probability distribution of any estimator in principle, although the actual mathematical details in doing so may be difficult. The criteria we shall use to judge estimators will be based on properties of the probability distribution of the statistic $t_j(X_1, X_2, \ldots, X_N)$ which is an estimator of θ_j. The properties are:

Definition 2-2-1. A statistic $t_j(X_1, X_2, \ldots, X_N)$ is a *consistent estimator* of θ_j if and only if

$$\underset{N \to \infty}{\text{Lim}} \, P\left\{|t_j(X_1, X_2, \ldots, X_N) - \theta_j| < \epsilon\right\} = 1$$

for any arbitrary $\epsilon > 0$ and all values of θ_j in the parameter space.

Definition 2-2-2. A statistic $t_j(X_1, X_2, \ldots, X_N)$ is an *unbiased estimator* of θ_j if and only if the expected value

$$E(t_j(X_1, X_2, \ldots, X_N)) = \theta_j$$

for all values of N and all values of θ in the parameter space. The difference $E(t_j(X_1, X_2, \ldots, X_N)) - \theta_j$ is called the *bias* in the estimator.

Definition 2-2-3. A statistic $t_j^*(X_1, X_2, \ldots, X_N)$ is a minimum variance estimator of θ_j

$$\text{Var}\,(t_j^*(X_1, X_2, \ldots, X_N)) \le \text{Var}\,(t_j(X_1, X_2, \ldots, X_N))$$

for all values of N and all statistics $t_j(X_1, X_2, \ldots, X_N)$.

The basic concept underlying the property of consistency is that as we increase the sample size we want our estimator to be very close to the true parameter value for any possible realization of the sample values. If we have a consistent estimator then, as the sample size becomes larger, with certainty the estimator will differ from the true value of the parameter by an amount no greater than ϵ which can be chosen arbitrarily small. This property is intuitively reasonable and any estimator which does not possess it will usually be discarded because increased sampling should eventually lead us to the correct value. We must insist that this property hold for all values of θ_j in the parameter space since there are some estimators which behave very well for certain points in the parameter space and not for others.

As an extreme example, we may take $t(X_1, X_2, \ldots, X_N) = 1$, in Problem 1-1-2, as the estimator for μ_0. Certainly if $\mu_0 = 1$ this estimator is excellent, but if $\mu_0 = 100$ it is very poor.

As an example of a consistent estimator, consider estimator $\bar{X}_N$ of μ_0 in Problem 1-1-2. By Chebyshev's inequality:

$$P(|\bar{X}_N - E(\bar{X}_N)| < k\sqrt{\text{Var}(\bar{X}_N)}) > 1 - \frac{1}{k^2} \qquad (2\text{-}2\text{-}1)$$

Since $\bar{X}_N$ is normally distributed with mean μ_0 and variance $1/N$ we have, from (2-2-1), that

$$P\left(|\bar{X}_N - \mu_0| < \frac{k}{\sqrt{N}}\right) > 1 - \frac{1}{k^2} \qquad (2\text{-}2\text{-}2)$$

and by selecting $k = \epsilon\sqrt{N}$ we obtain

$$P(|\bar{X}_N - \mu_0| < \epsilon) > 1 - \frac{1}{\epsilon^2 N} \qquad (2\text{-}2\text{-}3)$$

From 2-2-3 we see that as $N \to \infty$ the righthand side approaches one, which implies that $\bar{X}_N$ is a consistent estimator of μ_0. To exhibit another estimator of μ_0, which is not consistent, we take X_N, the last drawn sample observation. Clearly, no matter how large we choose N, we will only have one observation from which our estimate is computed. Therefore the increased sample size will not use more than one observation for the estimation of μ_0.

Consider, now, the implications of the property of unbiasedness. Suppose $t(X_1, X_2, \ldots, X_N)$ is an unbiased estimator of θ. If we take M samples each of size N, where we denote the outcome of the jth sample by $x_{1j}, x_{2j}, \ldots, x_{Nj}$, then $1/M \sum_{j=1}^{M} t(x_{1j}, x_{2j}, \ldots, x_{Nj})$ will be approximately equal to θ for large M. That is, the average value of the estimates for a large number of samples will be close to the parameter θ. The property of unbiasedness does not insure that any single estimate will be close to the true parameter value however.

In Problem 1-1-2 we have taken $\bar{X}_N$ as an estimator of μ_0. To show that it is an unbiased estimator of μ_0 we find that the expected value

$$E\left(\sum_{i=1}^{N} (X_i/N)\right) = \frac{1}{N} \sum_{i=1}^{N} E(X_i) = \frac{N\mu_0}{N} = \mu_0$$

To verify the property of unbiasedness, it is not necessary to determine the entire probability distribution of the estimator since expected values can be computed from a knowledge of the distribution of the X_i, $i = 1$, $2, \ldots, N$.

Let us now examine $\sigma(X_1, X_2, \ldots, X_N) = \sum_{i=1}^{N} (X_i - \bar{X}_N)^2/N$ as an estimator of the parameter σ^2, where each X_i is normally distributed with mean μ and variance σ^2. To show it is not an unbiased estimator, we let $N = 2$. This estimator becomes

$$\sigma(X_1, X_2) = \frac{1}{2}\left[\left(X_1 - \frac{X_1 + X_2}{2}\right)^2 + \left(X_2 - \frac{X_1 + X_2}{2}\right)^2\right]$$
$$- \frac{1}{8}(X_1 \quad X_2)^2 + (X_2 - X_1)^2$$

Recall that linear combinations of independent normal random variables are normally distributed with the appropriate mean and variance. It follows, then, that the random variables $X_1 - X_2$ and $X_2 - X_1$ are normally distributed with mean $E(X_1 - X_2) = 0$ and variance $\text{Var}(X_1 - X_2) = 2\sigma^2$. Since $X_1 - X_2$ has mean 0, $E(X_1 - X_2)^2 = \text{Var}(X_1 - X_2) = 2\sigma^2$. Hence,

$$E(\sigma(X_1, X_2)) - \frac{1}{8}[E((X_1 - X_2)^2) + E((X_2 - X_1)^2)]$$
$$= \frac{1}{8}(2\sigma^2 + 2\sigma^2)$$
$$= \frac{\sigma^2}{2}$$

So $\sigma(X_1, X_2, \ldots, X_N)$ is not an unbiased estimator of σ^2. It can be shown, however, that $N\sigma(X_1, X_2, \ldots, X_N)/N - 1 = \sum_{i=1}^{N} (X_i - \bar{X})^2/N - 1$ is an unbiased estimator of σ^2. As in this case, it is common that a biased estimator can be made unbiased by a slight alteration of the estimator.

Unbiased estimators are most important in cases of repeated estimation of the same parameter. But let us examine a case in which an unbiased estimator may not be desirable.

Problem 2-2-1. A farmer hires a group of teenagers to pick strawberries for him. They are told that they will be paid $.01 for each ounce they pick, with the farmer judging the weight. The pickers are provided with baskets which, when full, contain 51 ounces of strawberries. (Assume that each basket will be filled as much as possible). So at the end of the day, when the pickers return with their baskets, the farmer must estimate the weight of each basket and pay each person accordingly.

We shall consider three estimators for the weight of the strawberries: The first estimates every basket as weighing 51 ounces which is exactly correct, since every basket is assumed to be exactly full. In probabilistic terms, we estimate 51 ounces with probability one and, therefore, this estimator is an unbiased estimator of the true weight. The farmer, however, does not like this estimator since he would need a lot of change to make the payments, and so he proposes a second estimator. The second estimates the weight to be 100 ounces if, from a table of random numbers between 1 and 100, a number between 1 and 51 is drawn; if a number between 52 and 100 is drawn, the estimator estimates the weight to be zero. In probabilistic terms the estimator assigns probability .51 to a weight of 100, and .49 to a weight of 0. The expected value of this estimator is $0(.49) + 100(.51) = .51$ ounces. Hence, this is an unbiased estimator even though it never will guess the true value exactly. From the farmer's point of view it is desirable, since he avoids the need for a lot of change to make his payments, and if he has a large number of payments to make, he will pay an average of about $.51 per basket.

The teenagers are a little disturbed over this estimator and ask the farmer to use the first estimator. He refuses, but he offers a compromise which is the third estimator. This one will estimate the weight of each basket as 50 ounces—biased in favor of the farmer who insists he will make no other offers since the second estimator is fair to all concerned. (The teenager, on the other hand, may reason that he has worked all day and now faces the prospect of going home without any money.)

The point of this example is that unbiasedness is not the only property that one should consider in an estimator. One may, for good reason, choose an estimator which is biased—such as the third estimator. In this case, it would assure the reward for a day's work.

Since unbiasedness does not insure that an estimate is close to the true value of the parameter being estimated, we might try an estimator with the property of minimum variance. But that would bring us no closer to the true value, as we can see from the last example. The third estimator will have minimum variance since it has variance zero, but it never estimates the true value correctly. The difficulty of merely having a minimum variance estimator is that the variance of an estimator is a measure of the deviation from its expected value rather than the parameter which it is trying to estimate. Thus, we are led to:

Definition 2-2-4. If $t_j(X_1, X_2, \ldots, X_N)$ is an estimator of θ_j then the *mean square error* (M. S. E.) of the estimator is defined as $E(t_j(X_1, X_2, \ldots, X_N) - \theta_j)^2$.

From this definition we obtain the important relationship

$$M. S. E. = E[t_j(X_1, X_2, \ldots, X_N) - \theta_j]^2$$
$$= E\{t_j(X_1, X_2, \ldots, X_N) - E(t_j(X_1, X_2, \ldots, X_N))$$
$$+ E(t_j(X_1, X_2, \ldots, X_N)) - \theta_j\}^2$$
$$= E[t_j(X_1, X_2, \ldots, X_N) - E(t_j(X_1, X_2, \ldots, X_N))]^2$$
$$+ [E(t_j(X_1, X_2, \ldots, X_N)) - \theta_j]^2$$
$$\text{Variance} + (\text{bias})^2 \qquad (2\text{-}2\text{-}4)$$

So the M. S. E. will always be greater than the variance, and in the special case of an unbiased estimator, the two will be the same. We therefore combine the concepts of minimum variance and unbiasedness in:

Definition 2-2-5. An estimator $t_j(X_1, X_2, \ldots, X_N)$ for θ_j is an *unbiased minimum variance* (U. M. V.) estimator if among all unbiased estimators it has the smallest variance.

If we now examine the three estimators proposed to solve Problem 2-2-1 in terms of their mean square error instead of their variance, we will get a more meaningful comparison. Since the first estimator is unbiased and has zero variance, it will have zero M. S. E. The second estimator has a zero bias and variance equal to $.49(.51)^2 + .51(.49)^2 - .2499$ which is also its M. S. E. The third estimator has a bias of .01 and variance of zero which will yield a M. S. E. of .0001. If we prefer estimators with small mean square error, our order of preference would be estimators one, three, two.

Since the mean square error in the case of an unbiased estimator is equivalent to a minimum variance estimator, we will now consider the problem of determining when an unbiased estimator is a U. M. V. estimator. We have shown that $\bar{X}_N$ is an unbiased estimator μ_0, in Problem 1-1-2, but is it an U. M. V. estimator? Our answer could be affirmative if we knew that the smallest variance an unbiased estimator of μ_0 could attain is $1/N$. Because $\bar{X}_N$ has variance $1/N$, it would be a U. M. V. estimator. The following theorem permits us to set a lower bound on the variance of an unbiased estimator.

Theorem 2-2-1. *Cramir-Rao:* Let $X_1, X_2, \ldots, X_N$ be a random sample from a population have density function $f(x, \theta)$. Assume that $t(X_1, X_2, \ldots, X_N)$ is an unbiased estimator of θ. Then

$$\text{Var}(t(X_1, X_2, \ldots, X_N)) \geq \frac{1}{NE(\delta \log f(x, \theta)/\delta\theta)^2}$$
$$= \frac{1}{-NE(\delta^2 \log f(x, \theta)/\delta\theta^2)} \qquad (2\text{-}2\text{-}5)$$

The denominator of (2-2-5) is sometimes called the amount of information on θ contained in $X_1, X_2, \ldots, X_N$. This quantity depends upon N and $f(x, \theta)$, not upon the estimator. The lower bound given by (2-2-5) may not be attained by any unbiased estimator. Thus, if we exhibit an estimator whose variance is greater than the Cramir-Rao* lower bound, we cannot immediately conclude that it is not a U. M. V. estimator.

We can show that $\bar{X}_N$ is a U. M. V. estimator for μ_0 by showing that the lower bound of (2-2-5) is equal to $\mathrm{var}(\bar{X}_N) = 1/N$. Since $\log f(X, \mu_0) = -(X - \mu_0)^2/2$ for a normal distribution with mean μ_0 and variance one, $\delta^2 \log f(X, \mu_0)/\delta \mu_0^2 = -1$, from which the result follows immediately.

Another concept closely associated with the concept of a U. M. V. estimator is that of an *efficient estimator*.

Definition 2-2-6. An estimator $t(X_1, X_2, \ldots, X_N)$ of the parameter θ is said to be an *efficient estimator* if its variance equals the Cramir-Rao lower bound for the particular density (mass) function under consideration.

From previous remarks, it is possible that a U. M. V. estimator is not an efficient estimator but an efficient estimator is always a U. M. V. Since the U. M. V. estimator $\bar{X}_N$ for the parameter $\bar{X}_N$ has variance equal to the Cramir-Rao lower bound it is an efficient estimator.

We now have defined several criteria for judging estimators, and we have indicated how one can proceed to verify these properties. Although these are all properties of the probability distribution of the estimator, it will not usually be necessary to find this distribution to verify them. In fact, what we now seek are general methods of constructing estimators which will automatically have these desirable properties. The next two sections will present two general methods of estimation which yield estimators with some of these properties.

2-3. MAXIMUM LIKELIHOOD ESTIMATION

One general method of constructing estimators is the method of maximum likelihood. The method chooses as estimators of the parameters θ_j $j = 1, 2, \ldots, m$, a set of statistics which maximize the likelihood function for the given sample values. Since for a given set of sample values the likelihood function gives the probability of obtaining

*Since we have only defined the Cramir-Rao lower bound where the density function depends upon only one parameter, we do not consider the estimation of any one of m parameters θ_j.

these values, or the corresponding density function, it is intuitively a desirable property to choose the unknown parameters in a manner which makes that probability as large as possible. But we must consider how well these estimators satisfy the criteria established in the previous section. Therefore, we will first examine their method of construction and then show that these estimators have desirable properties.

Restricting our discussion to density functions which depend upon only one parameter, the likelihood function has the form

$$g(\theta) = \prod_{i=1}^{N} f(x_i, \theta) \qquad \theta \in \Omega \qquad (2\text{-}3\text{-}1)$$

where we denote the parameter space by Ω. To maximize the function $g(\theta)$ for $\theta \in \Omega$ we can use the methods of calculus if Ω is an interval of real numbers and $g(\theta)$ is a differentiable function.* If these conditions do not hold, the method of maximum likelihood can still be applied by returning to the basic definition of the maximum of a function $g(\theta)$ for $\theta \in \Omega$. For example, if Ω consists of two values θ_0 and θ_1, then the maximum likelihood estimate is found to be θ_0 where

$$g(\theta_0) = \prod_{i=1}^{N} f(x_i, \theta_0) > \prod_{i=1}^{N} f(x_i, \theta_1) = g(\theta_1) \qquad (2\text{-}3\text{-}2)$$

and θ_1 where the reverse inequality holds. (We assume that equalities will occur with probability zero, and so usually we will ignore that possibility.) Similarly if Ω consists of K values $\theta_0, \theta_1, \ldots, \theta_{K-1}$, then we find the maximum value of $g(\theta)$ for $\theta = \theta_j, j = 0, 1, \ldots, K - 1$, and choose as our maximum likelihood estimate the value θ_j for which the maximum of $g(\theta)$ is attained. In these cases, the form of the estimator cannot be given in terms of a mathematical function. For example, consider the likelihood function in the form

$$g(\theta) = \theta^{\sum_{i=1}^{4} x_i} (1 - \theta)^{4 - \sum_{i=1}^{4} x_i} \qquad \theta \in \Omega \qquad (2\text{-}3\text{-}3)$$

where $X_1 = 1, X_2 = 0, X_3 = 1, X_4 = 1$ and $\Omega = (1/4, 1/2, 3/4) = (\theta_0, \theta_1, \theta_2)$. This is the type of function which arose in Problem 1-1-3, and which generally occurs when each observation $X_i, i = 1, 2, \ldots, N$ is an independent Bernoulli random variable with $P\{X_i = 1\} = \theta$ and $P\{X_i = 0\} = 1 - \theta$. We then obtain that $g(\theta_0) = (1/4)^3 (3/4)^1 = 3/256$, $g(\theta_1) = (1/2)^3 (1/2)^1 = 16/256, g(\theta_2) = (3/4)^3 (1/4)^1 = 27/256$. Therefore $g(\theta_2)$ yields the maximum value of $g(\theta)$ for this particular sample, and the maximum likelihood estimate of θ is 3/4. Note that in this example the likelihood function depends only upon the value $\sum_{i=1}^{4} x_i = 3$. By similar

---

*The expression $\Omega \in \theta$ is read "θ belongs to Ω" and the expression $\theta \notin \Omega$ is read "θ does not belong to Ω."

calculations we can compute the value of the maximum likelihood estimate for all possible values $\sum_{i=1}^{4} x_i$ and, doing so, we obtain an estimator of the form

$$t(X_1, X_2, X_3, X_4) = \begin{cases} \dfrac{3}{4} & \text{if } \sum_{i=1}^{4} X_i = 3, \sum_{i=1}^{4} X_i = 4 \\[2mm] \dfrac{1}{2} & \text{if } \sum_{i=1}^{4} X_i = 2 \\[2mm] \dfrac{1}{4} & \text{if } \sum_{i=1}^{4} X_i = 0, \sum_{i=1}^{4} X_i = 1 \end{cases} \qquad (2\text{-}3\text{-}4)$$

We now must investigate some of the criteria of good estimators which are based on the probability mass function of the estimator given in (2-3-4). Recalling that $\sum_{i=1}^{N} X_i$ is a binomial random vaiable with parameters N and θ if each $X_i, i = 1, 2, \ldots, N$ is an independent Bernoulli random variable with parameter θ, then

$$P\{t(X_1, X_2, X_3, X_4) = 3/4\} = P\left\{\sum_{i=1}^{4} X_i = 3\right\} + P\left\{\sum_{i=1}^{4} X_i = 4\right\}$$
$$= 4\theta^3(1 - \theta) + \theta^4$$
$$P\{t(X_1, X_2, X_3, X_4) = 1/2\} = P\left\{\sum_{i=1}^{4} X_i = 2\right\} = 6\theta^2(1 - \theta)^2$$
$$P\{t(X_1, X_2, X_3, X_4) = 1/4\} = P\left\{\sum_{i=1}^{4} X_i = 0\right\} + P\left\{\sum_{i=1}^{4} X_i = 1\right\}$$
$$= (1 - \theta)^4 + 4\theta(1 - \theta)^3 \qquad (2\text{-}3\text{-}5)$$

To verify whether the estimator defined in (2-3-4) is unbiased we must verify that its expected value equals θ for all $\theta \in \Omega$. From the probability mass function given in (2-3-5) we can compute the expected value of the estimator to be

$$E(t(X_1, X_2, X_3, X_4)) = \frac{3}{4}(4\theta^3(1 - \theta) + \theta^4)$$
$$+ \frac{1}{2}(6^2(1 - \theta)^2)$$
$$+ \frac{1}{4}((1 - \theta)^4 + 4\theta(1 - \theta)^3) \qquad (2\text{-}3\text{-}6)$$

Now if (2-3-6) equals θ for all $\theta \in \Omega$, the estimator is unbiased. If we consider the case where $\theta = \theta_1 = \frac{1}{2}$, we obtain by substitution in (2-3-6) that $E(t(X_1, X_2, X_3, X_4)) = \frac{1}{2}$. But if we consider the case where $\theta = \theta_0 = \frac{1}{4}$, we obtain by substitution in (2-3-6) that $E(t(X_1, X_2, X_3, X_4)) = \frac{21}{64}$, and the estimator is therefore biased. This illustrates that although maximum likelihood estimators are constructed by an intuitively reasonable procedure, that procedure does not guarantee they will satisfy the criteria which we consider important.

In general, for most of the usual statistical problems, the parameter space Ω is an interval and $g(\theta)$ is differentiable, so we can apply the techniques of the calculus. The procedure is to find a value of $\theta \in \Omega$ which makes $dg(\theta)/d\theta$ equal to zero and whose second derivative is negative at that point. This procedure is modified slightly and we consider $\log g(\theta)$, rather than $g(\theta)$, and seek values of $\theta \in \Omega$ which make $d \log g(\theta)/d\theta$ zero and whose second derivative is negative at this point.* The two procedures are equivalent; for

$$\frac{d \log g(\theta)}{d\theta} = \frac{1}{g(\theta)} \frac{dg(\theta)}{d\theta} \tag{2-3-7}$$

Also, $g(\theta) > 0$ since $g(\theta) = \prod_{i=1}^{N} f(x_i, \theta)$ where $f(x_i, \theta) > 0$. Therefore (2-3-7) can be made equal to zero only if $dg(\theta)/d\theta$ equals 0. For values of θ which make (2-3-7) equal to zero, the condition that they be relative maximum is that the second derivative be negative at those points. Computing the second derivative we obtain

$$\frac{d^2 \log g(\theta)}{d\theta^2} = \frac{1}{g(\theta)} \frac{d^2 g(\theta)}{d\theta^2} - \frac{dg(\theta)}{d\theta}\left(\frac{1}{g(\theta)}\right)^2 \tag{2-3-8}$$

Evaluating this expression at a value $\theta = \theta_0$ where $dg(\theta)/d\theta|_{\theta=\theta_0} = 0$ we obtain

$$\frac{d^2 \log g(\theta)}{d\theta^2}\bigg|_{\theta=\theta_0} = \frac{1}{g(\theta_0)} \frac{d^2 g(\theta)}{d\theta^2}\bigg|_{\theta=\theta_0} \tag{2-3-9}$$

This last expression can be negative only if the second factor on the right is negative since $g(\theta_0) > 0$. The advantage of considering $\log g(\theta)$, rather than $g(\theta)$, is evident since $g(\theta)$ is a product of density or mass function, whereas $\log g(\theta)$ is a sum of density or mass function, and the differentiation of a sum is much easier than that of a product.

Now consider the problem of finding the maximum likelihood estimator of the parameter θ, where the population is normal with mean θ and variance one. If we have a random sample of size N from this population, the likelihood function is given by

$$g(\theta) = \prod_{i=1}^{N} \frac{1}{\sqrt{2\pi}} e^{-1/2(x_i-\theta)^2} \qquad -\infty < \theta < \infty$$

$$= \left[\frac{1}{\sqrt{2\pi}}\right]^N e^{-1/2 \sum_{i=1}^{N}(x_i-\theta)^2} \tag{2-3-10}$$

To find the maximum likelihood estimator we consider

$$\log g(\theta) = N \log\left[\frac{1}{\sqrt{2\pi}}\right] + \frac{1}{2} \sum_{i=1}^{N}(x_i - \theta)^2 \tag{2-3-11}$$

---

*We always use the log to denote the natural logarithm.

and compute

$$\frac{d \log g(\theta)}{d\theta} = \sum_{i=1}^{N} (x_i - \theta) \qquad (2\text{-}3\text{-}12)$$

Setting (2-3-12) equal to zero, we obtain the solution $\theta = \sum_{i=1}^{N} X_i/N$. This is the maximum likelihood estimator since at all values of θ the second derivative will equal minus one. Recall from Section 2-2 that this estimator is unbiased and a U. M. V. estimator.

Consider next a likelihood function of the type defined in (2-3-3).

$$g(\theta) = \theta^{\sum_{i=1}^{N} X_i} (1 - \theta)^{N - \sum_{i=1}^{N} X_i} \qquad \theta \in \Omega \qquad (2\text{-}3\text{-}13)$$

where Ω the parameter space is the closed interval $0 \leq \theta \leq 1$. Following the procedure of the last example we obtain

$$\text{Log } g(\theta) = \sum_{i=1}^{N} X_i \log \theta + \left(N - \sum_{i=1}^{N} X_i\right) \log (1 - \theta) \qquad (2\text{-}3\text{-}14)$$

and

$$\frac{d \log g(\theta)}{d\theta} = \sum_{i=1}^{N} X_i/\theta - \left(N - \sum_{i=1}^{N} X_i\right)/(1 - \theta) \qquad (2\text{-}3\text{-}15)$$

Setting (2-3-15) equal to zero and solving for θ, we obtain as the maximum likelihood estimator $\sum_{i=1}^{N} X_i/N$, which we will denote by $\hat{\theta}_N$. Now we will verify that $\hat{\theta}_N$ is an unbiased estimator. This readily follows from the fact that $\sum_{i=1}^{N} X_i$ is a binomial random variable with parameters N and θ and therefore $E(\hat{\theta}_N) = 1/N \ E(\sum_{i=1}^{N} X_i) = 1/N(N\theta) = \theta$. Further, we have $\text{var}(\hat{\theta}_N) = 1/N^2 \ \text{var}(\sum_{i=1}^{N} X_i) = N\theta(1 - \theta)/N^2 = \theta(1 - \theta)/N$. To verify that $\hat{\theta}_N$ is a U. M. V. estimator, we must show that the Cramir-Rao lower bound equals $\theta(1 - \theta)/N$. The probability mass function associated with each independent random variable X_i in the random sample of size N is

$$f(X, \theta) = \theta^X (1 - \theta)^{1-x} \qquad \begin{array}{c} X = 0, 1 \\ 0 \leq \theta \leq 1 \end{array} \qquad (2\text{-}3\text{-}16)$$

from which we obtain

$$\text{Log } f(X, \theta) = X \log \theta + (1 - X) \log (1 - \theta) \qquad (2\text{-}3\text{-}17)$$

and therefore

$$\frac{d \log f(X, \theta)}{d\theta} = \frac{X}{\theta} - \frac{(1 - X)}{1 - \theta}$$

$$= \frac{(X - \theta)}{\theta(1 - \theta)} \qquad (2\text{-}3\text{-}18)$$

Now computing the denominator of (2-2-5) we have

$$NE\left\{\left|\frac{d\log f(X,\theta)}{d\theta}\right|^2\right\} = NE\left\{\frac{(X-\theta)^2}{\theta^2(1-\theta)^2}\right\}$$

$$= \frac{N}{\theta^2(1-\theta)^2}\,\mathrm{Var}(X)$$

$$= \frac{N}{\theta^2(1-\theta)^2}\theta(1-\theta)$$

$$= \frac{N}{\theta(1-\theta)} \tag{2-3-19}$$

which illustrates that $\mathrm{var}\,\boldsymbol{\theta}_N$ equals the Cramir-Rao lower bound.

It would, of course, be convenient to know what good properties all maximum likelihood estimators will possess. We know they do not necessarily have to be unbiased, but do they have to be consistent? They do, under very mild restriction upon the density function. In general, the maximum likelihood estimators have the following desirable properties:

1. Maximum likelihood estimators are consistent.
2. Maximum likelihood estimators for large sample sizes, N, are approximately normally distributed, with mean θ and variance

$$\left[NE\left\{\left(\frac{d\log f(X,\theta)}{d\theta}\right)^2\right\}\right]^{-1}$$

The good properties of maximum likelihood estimation only hold in general for large sample sizes. For small sample sizes, each estimator must separately be verified for unbiasedness and minimum variance properties.

Finally, consider the relationship between maximum likelihood estimators and sufficient statistics. In the case where a sufficient statistic $t(X_1, X_2, \ldots, X_N)$ exists for a density function $f(x, \theta)$, the likelihood function has the form

$$g(\theta) = h(X_1, X_2, \ldots, X_N)k(t, \theta) \tag{2-3-20}$$

and

$$\mathrm{Log}\,g(\theta) = \log h(X_1, X_2, \ldots, X_N) + \log k(t, \theta) \tag{2-3-21}$$

Since the second term on the right of (2-3-21) is the only term that depends upon θ, it must be maximized in order to maximize the entire expression. This term, however, depends only upon t and θ, and so the choice of θ which will maximize $g(\theta)$ depends upon $t(X_1, X_2, \ldots, X_N)$. Therefore if a sufficient statistic exists, the maximum likelihood estimator will be a function of that statistic.

2–4. LEAST SQUARES ESTIMATION

The method of least squares is an important method of estimation for a special type of partially specified probabilistic model. This model is more general than the models considered in Problems 1-1-1, 1-1-2, and 1-1-3, since it is not necessary to specify the functional form of the probability density function or the probability mass function. On the other hand, it is essential that the expected values of the random variables under consideration have a special structure so that, in this respect, the model will be more specialized. To illustrate the type of model that least squares estimation deals with, consider:

Problem 2-4-1. An automobile manufacturer believes that there is a relationship between personal income, x, and expenditure on automobiles, Y. If he could determine this relationship, he would better be able to predict the demand for his product.

The first consideration in developing the model to describe this relationship is: For different people, each with the same amount of personal income, x, the expenditure on automobiles, Y, may be different. We will be concerned, for simplicity, only with people having incomes (x) between $5,500 and $12,500. In addition, we will group those with incomes between $5,500 and $6,499.99 as having an income of $6,000; those with incomes between $6,500 and $7,499.99 as having an income of $7,000; etc. Thus, we will have seven groups of people and, in each group, all will have the same personal income, but different expenditures on automobiles. Another way of stating this is that we have seven populations, where the attribute under consideration is the expenditure on automobiles and the characteristic is the amount in dollars. According to the manufacturer's economist, we may assume that the average value of the amount expended on automobiles in each population can be represented by an expression of the form $a + bx$, where a and b are unknown but are the same for each population. The unknown parameters in this linear relationship are the quantities to be estimated by taking observations.

This model differs from those previously considered in that we are concerned with several populations simultaneously. To estimate the unknown parameters, a reasonable first step would be to take a random sample of size $n_i (i = 1, 2, \ldots, 7)$ from each population. We will consider only the case where all $n_i = 1$ to illustrate the procedures. The random sample would consist of seven observations, where the observation from a population with income x_i is denoted by $Y_{x_i} (i = 1, 2, \ldots, 7)$, and we will assume that these random variables are mutually independent.* In addition, assume that the variability about the mean for each population is a constant value σ^2. Summarizing, we have

$$E(Y_{x_i}) = a + bx_i \qquad i = 1, 2, \ldots, 7$$
$$\text{Var}(Y_{x_i}) = \sigma^2 \qquad i = 1, 2, \ldots, 7 \qquad (2\text{-}4\text{-}1)$$
$$Y_{x_i} \text{ are mutually independent } i = 1, 2, \ldots, 7$$

Nowhere have we made any assumptions concerning the form of the density function. But we shall denote the density function associated with the population with income x_i by $f_{x_i}(y, a, b, \sigma^2)$ since we know there are three unknown parameters where the density function may have different functional forms for different values of x_i. The likelihood function for the particular sample $Y_{x_i} = y_i \; i = 1, 2, \ldots, 7$ is given by

$$g(a, b, \sigma^2) = \prod_{i=1}^{7} f_{x_i}(y_i, a, b, \sigma^2) \qquad (2\text{-}4\text{-}2)$$

The fact that the density function is not specified precludes the use of maximum likelihood estimation. Instead we will use the principle of least squares, which states that we should choose as estimates of a and b the values $\hat{a}$ and $\hat{b}$ which minimize

$$S(a, b) = \sum_{i=1}^{7} y_{x_i} - (a + bx_i))^2 \qquad (2\text{-}4\text{-}3)$$

From calculus, we know that this can be achieved by solving

$$\frac{\delta S(a, b)}{\delta a} = -2 \sum_{i=1}^{7} (y_{x_i} - (a + bx_i)) = 0$$
$$\frac{\delta S(a, b)}{\delta b} = -2 \sum_{i=1}^{7} (y_{x_i} - (a + bx_i))x_i = 0 \qquad (2\text{-}4\text{-}4)$$

and taking for the values $\hat{a}$ and $\hat{b}$ the solutions of these two equations. The equations (2-4-4) are called, in the terminology of least squares estimation, the *normal equations*. In this case the normal equations have a unique solution given by

$$\hat{b} = \frac{\sum_{i=1}^{7} (x_i - \bar{x})(y_{x_i} - \bar{y})}{\sum_{i=1}^{7} (x_i - \bar{x})^2}$$
$$\hat{a} = \bar{y} - \hat{b}\bar{x} \qquad (2\text{-}4\text{-}5)$$

where $\bar{x} = \sum_{i=1}^{7} x_i/7$, $\bar{y} = \sum_{i=1}^{7} y_{x_i}/7$, and y_{x_i} are the observed expenditures on automobiles for each income level x_i. The *normal equations* for the general case do not necessarily have a unique solution given by an algebraic

---

*It is only necessary to assume that all the random variables are uncorrelated to justify the desirable properties of the least squares estimators, but for simplicity we will assume the stronger property of mutual independence.

formula, as in (2-4-5); but any solution to the normal equations will be called a least squares estimate. To estimate the unknown variance σ^2, we interpret the variance as a measure of the average squared derivation of a random variable from its expectation. Since the estimate of the expected value of Y_{x_i} is $\hat{a} + \hat{b}x_i$, we take as the estimator of σ^2

$$\hat{\sigma}^2 = \frac{\sum_{i=1}^{7} (y_{x_i} - (\hat{a} + \hat{b}x_i))^2}{5} \qquad (2\text{-}4\text{-}6)$$

where the divisor $N - 2 = 5$ is used, in order that $\hat{\sigma}^2$ be an unbiased estimator.

i	x_i	y_{x_i}	$x_i - \bar{x}$	$y_{x_i} - \bar{y}$	$(x_i - \bar{x})^2$	$(x_i - \bar{x})(y_{x_i} - \bar{y})$
1	6,000	1,700	−3,000	−500	9,000,000	1,500,000
2	7,000	1,800	−2,000	−400	4,000,000	800,000
3	8,000	2,000	−1,000	−200	1,000,000	200,000
4	9,000	2,000	0	0	0	0
5	10,000	2,400	1,000	200	1,000,000	200,000
6	11,000	2,600	2,000	400	4,000,000	800,000
7	12,000	2,700	3,000	500	9,000,000	1,500,000
Totals	63,000	15,400	0	0	28,000,000	5,000,000

FIGURE 2-4-1. Least square calculations for automobile expenditure problem

If we actually performed the experiment of selecting a person from each income group and determining his expenditures, the results would appear as in Figure 2-4-1. From the results in the totals row of Figure 2-4-1 we obtain, by substitution in (2-4-5), that $\hat{b} = \frac{5,000,000}{28,000,000} = 5/28$ and $\hat{a} = 2200 - \frac{5}{28}(9000) = \$593$. So the expected expenditure on automobiles for a person with income x_i is given by $\$593 + \frac{5}{28}x_i$. (We must be careful not to be too eager to extend this result to all values of x_i since we only made the assumptions necessary to obtain this estimate for seven income groups. It is tempting however to conclude for example that if a person has no income, $x_i = 0$, then the average expenditure on automobiles will be $\$593$.) This type of problem is called an *extrapolation* problem, that is, we wish to predict the expected value of Y_{x_i} beyond the values x_i for which we were able to take observation. It is not essential to observe the value of Y_{x_i} for the particular x_i, but merely to be able to assume that $E(Y_{x_i}) = a + bx_i$, where the values of a and b are the same as for all observed random variables Y_{x_i}. Since b is the rate of change of the expected value of Y_{x_i} with respect to x_i, it is unlikely that it will remain the same for all values of x_i; so the estimate $E(y_0) = \$593$ is probably not valid since the assumptions of the model do not apply.

The extrapolation problem occurs quite frequently if the x_i values correspond to instants in chronological time. Consider the following problem:

Problem 2-4-2. Now that the automobile manufacturer knows the relationship between the expenditure for automobiles and the personal income of people within the $6,000 to $12,000 income range, he now would like to estimate the personal income of various groups of people (for example factory workers, policemen, etc.) for the next year, in order to predict the demand for automobiles and plan his production schedules. To establish a probability model for a particular group—factory workers— we denote the yearly personal income in year t by Z_t, taking the present to be year 0. Assume

$$E(Z_t) = c + dt \qquad t = -4, -3, -2, -1, 0, 1$$
$$\mathrm{Var}(Z_t) = \sigma^2 \tag{2-4-7}$$

and the random variables Z_t are mutually independent. We have explicitly assumed that this model applies to the income of factory workers for next year, $t = 1$. For each year, $t = -4, -3, -2, -1, 0$, we will select at random a factory worker to determine his personal income in that particular year. To satisfy the assumption of mutual independence of successive yearly incomes, it is necessary to select at random a different worker for each year. A similar condition would be necessary if we selected several workers in each year. Equations analogous to (2-4-5) may now be applied to obtain the least squares estimates of c and d—denoted by $\hat{c}$ and $\hat{d}$. We would then estimate the average income of factory workers for the next year by $E(Z_1) = \hat{c} + \hat{d}$. This extrapolation is valid since we assumed that the model is true for $t = 1$, although no value of Z_1 was available for the estimation of c and d.

We can now formulate a general probabilistic model with certain unspecified parameters where the method of least squares estimation is applied to estimate the unknown parameters.

Regression Model: Let $Y_{x_i} i = 1, 2, \ldots, N$ be N random variables such that

$$E(Y_{x_i}) = \sum_{j=1}^{P} B_j g_j(x_i) \tag{2-4-8}$$

$$\mathrm{Var}(Y_{x_i}) = \sigma^2 \tag{2-4-9}$$

$$E(Y_{x_i} - E(Y_{x_i}))(Y_{x_k} - E(Y_{x_k})) = 0$$
$$i \neq k \qquad i, k = 1, 2, \ldots, N \tag{2-4-10}$$

where all x_i are assumed different.

The relation (2-4-10) assumes that the random variables are uncorrelated, which is somewhat weaker than the assumption of independence made in the previous models of this section because independence implies lack of correlation but not conversely. The converse *is* true in the case that all random variables Y_{x_i} are normally distributed, but the assumption is not needed to apply these estimation procedures.* The model can readily be seen to include the previous model by selecting $p = 2$, $g_1(x_i) = 1$, and $g_2(x_i) = x_i$. If we select the functions $g_j(x_i) = x_i^{j-1}$, then we have a *polynomial regression model*.

We now state the *Principle of Least Squares:*
Any set of p values $\hat{B}_1, \hat{B}_2, \ldots, \hat{B}_p$ which minimize the expression

$$S(B_1, B_2, \ldots, B_p) = \sum_{i=1}^{N} \left(y_{x_i} - \left(\sum_{j=1}^{P} B_j g_j(x_i) \right) \right)^2$$

where y_{x_i} are the observed value of the random variables Y_{x_i} are considered least squares estimates of $B_1, B_2, \ldots, B_p$.
In order to find these values we form the *normal equations*

$$\frac{\delta S(B_1, B_2, \ldots, B_j, \ldots, B_p)}{\delta B_j} = \sum_{i=1}^{N} g_j(x_i)(y_{x_i} - \sum_{j=1}^{P} B_j g_j(x_i)) = 0$$

$$j = 1, 2, \cdots, p \qquad\qquad (2\text{-}4\text{-}11)$$

Any set of solutions to these equations will be *least squares estimates*.
A general model and a method of obtaining least squares estimates have now been considered. But do the estimates so obtained have any good properties? These estimators are *linear estimators*, and by a linear estimator we mean that the estimator $\hat{B}_{j'}$ of $B_{j'}$ can be written

$$\hat{B}_{j'} = \sum_{i=1}^{N} \gamma_i^{(j')} Y_{x_i}$$

That is, it can be written as a linear combination of the random variables Y_{x_i} where the coefficients $\gamma_i^{(j')}$ can depend upon the function $g_j(x_i)$ $j = 1, 2, \ldots, p$ but not upon the random variables Y_{x_i}. The estimator $\hat{b}$ in (2-4-5) has the form

$$\hat{b} = \frac{\sum_{i=1}^{N}(x_i - \bar{x})(Y_{x_i} - \bar{Y})}{\sum_{i=1}^{N}(x_i - \bar{x})^2} = \frac{\sum_{i=1}^{N}(x_i - \bar{x})Y_{x_i}}{\sum_{i=1}^{N}(x_i - \bar{x})^2} - \frac{\sum_{i=1}^{N}(x_i = \bar{x})\bar{Y}}{\sum_{i=1}^{N}(x_i - \bar{x})^2}$$

$$= \sum_{i=1}^{N} \frac{x_i - \bar{x}}{\sum_{i=1}^{N}(x_i - \bar{x})^2} Y_{x_i} \qquad\qquad (2\text{-}4\text{-}12)$$

*If we are interested in hypothesis testing problems, then it is necessary to assume that the random variables Y_{x_i} are normally distributed.

since the sum of the deviations about the mean is zero. We may then take $\gamma_i^{(b)} = (x_i - \bar{x})^2/\sum_{i=1}^{N}(x_i - \bar{x})^2$ to form the estimator $\sum_{i=1}^{N}\gamma_i^{(b)} Y_{x_i}$. Similarly, since

$$\hat{a} = \bar{Y} - \hat{b}\bar{x} = \sum_{i=1}^{N}\frac{1}{N}Y_{x_i} - \sum_{i=1}^{N}\bar{x}\gamma_i^{(b)}Y_{x_i}$$

$$= \sum_{i=1}^{N}\left(\frac{1}{N} - \bar{x}\gamma_i^{(b)}\right)\bar{Y}_{x_i} \qquad (2\text{-}4\text{-}13)$$

we may write the least squares estimator of a in the form $\sum_{i=1}^{N}\gamma_i^{(a)}\bar{Y}_{x_i}$ where $\gamma_i^{(a)} = 1/N - \bar{x}\gamma_i^{(b)}$.

Two good properties which least squares estimators possess are:

1. The least squares estimator for B_j is an unbiased estimator.
2. The least squares estimator for B_j has minimum variance among the class of all unbiased linear estimators of B_j.

To illustrate that $\sum_{i=1}^{N}\gamma_i^{(b)} Y_{x_i}$ is an unbiased estimator of b, note that

$$E\left(\sum_{i=1}^{N}\gamma_i^{(b)} Y_{x_i}\right) = \sum_{i=1}^{N}\gamma_i^{(b)} E(Y_{x_i})$$

$$= \sum_{i=1}^{N}\gamma_i^{(b)}(a + bx_i)$$

$$= \left(\sum_{i=1}^{N}\gamma_i^{(b)}\right)a + b\sum_{i=1}^{N}x_i\gamma_i^{(b)} \qquad (2\text{-}4\text{-}14)$$

$$\text{Now} \quad \sum_{i=1}^{N}\gamma_i^{(b)} = 0 \quad \text{and} \quad \sum_{i=1}^{N}\gamma_i^{(b)}x_i = 1$$

since

$$\sum_{i=1}^{N}x_i(x_i - \bar{x}) = \sum_{i=1}^{N}(x_i - \bar{x})^2$$

which shows that the estimator is unbiased. The concept of consistency which applies to repeated sampling from the same population does not apply to the model which we have assumed since we are taking a sample of size one from each population. Finally, we will take as our estimator of σ^2

$$\hat{\sigma}^2 = \sum_{i=1}^{N}\left(y_{x_i} - \left(\sum_{j=1}^{p}\hat{B}_j g_j(x_i)\right)\right)^2 / N - p \qquad (2\text{-}4\text{-}15)$$

where $\hat{B}_1, \hat{B}_2, \ldots, \hat{B}_p$ is any set of least squares estimates of $B_1, B_2, \ldots, B_p$. The estimator $\hat{\sigma}^2$ is an unbiased estimator of σ^2.

There is one case in which it is possible to compare the method of least squares estimation and the method of maximum likelihood estimation. It is that of the regression model stated in (2-4-8), (2-4-9), and (2-4-10) where the random variables Y_{x_i} are assumed, in addition, to be normally distributed. The likelihood function may then be written:

$$g(B_1, B_2, \ldots, B_p) = \prod_{i=1}^{N} \frac{1}{\sqrt{2\pi\sigma^2}} e^{-1/2\sigma^2 \left(y_{z_i} - \sum_{j=1}^{P} B_j g_j(x_i)\right)^2}$$

$$= \left(\frac{1}{\sqrt{2\pi\sigma^2}}\right)^N e^{-1/2\sigma^2 \sum_{i=1}^{N} \left(y_{z_i} - \left(\sum_{j=1}^{P} B_j g_j(x_i)\right)\right)^2} \quad (2\text{-}4\text{-}16)$$

In order to maximize the likelihood function it is necessary to make the exponent as small as possible. That is, we must minimize $\sum_{i=1}^{N} (y_{x_i} - (\sum_{j=1}^{P} B_j g_j(x_i))^2$. Thus, in this special case, the method of maximum likelihood estimation and the method of least squares estimation are equivalent.

2–5. OTHER METHODS OF ESTIMATION

The method described next is the *method of moments*. Assume that we have a random sample of size N from a population of density function $f(x, \theta_1, \theta_2, \ldots, \theta_m)$. We will denote the expected value of any observation raised to the kth power—the kth moment—by

$$E(X^k) = \mu_k(\theta_1, \theta_2, \ldots, \theta_m) \qquad k = 1, 2, \ldots \qquad (2\text{-}5\text{-}1)$$

where $\mu_k(\theta_1, \theta_2, \ldots, \theta_m)$ is a function of the unknown parameters. Thus, if the density function is given by

$$f(x, \theta_1, \theta_2) = \frac{1}{\sqrt{2\pi\theta_2}} e^{-(x-\theta_1)^2/2\theta_2} \qquad (2\text{-}5\text{-}2)$$

then

$$\mu_1(\theta_1, \theta_2) = \theta_1$$
$$\mu_2(\theta_1, \theta_2) = \theta_2 + \theta_1^2 \qquad (2\text{-}5\text{-}3)$$

We will define the kth sample moment for a random sample N by the relation

$$m_k = \sum_{i=1}^{N} X_i^k / N \qquad k = 1, 2, \ldots \qquad (2\text{-}5\text{-}4)$$

where, for any particular sample m_k will be a real number. The method of moments estimates the unknown parameters by setting up the p equations

$$m_k = \mu_k(\theta_1, \theta_2, \ldots, \theta_m) \qquad k = 1, 2, \ldots, p \qquad (2\text{-}5\text{-}5)$$

and solving for unknown parameters $\theta_1, \theta_2, \ldots, \theta_m$. Usually the number of equations p will equal the number of unknown parameters m, but generally we must take p large enough so that a solution to the system (2-5-5) exists. For the estimation of the parameters of the density given in (2-5-2), we take $p = m = 2$ and form

$$\frac{\sum\limits_{i=1}^{N} X_i}{N} = \theta_1 \qquad \frac{\sum\limits_{i=1}^{N} X_i^2}{N} = \theta_2 + \theta_1^2 \qquad (2\text{-}5\text{-}6)$$

The solution yields

$$\hat{\theta}_1 = \sum_{i=1}^{N} X_i/N = \bar{X}$$

and

$$\theta_2 = \frac{\sum\limits_{i=1}^{N} X_i^2}{N} - \left(\frac{\sum X_i}{N}\right)^2 = \sum_{i=1}^{N} (X_i - \bar{X})^2/N$$

which are the same as the maximum likelihood estimators.

This method of estimation is more general than the method of maximum likelihood, for we do not need to specify the entire density function but only the first p moments. In practice, however, it is not more general because these moments are computed from a knowledge of the density function. In the method of maximum likelihood, we may state that the estimators have some good properties such as consistency or asymptotic efficiency. The estimators obtained by the method of moments, in general, cannot be said to have any desirable properties; in practice, the method can yield estimators with good properties, but each case must be separately verified. Thus, we may say only that $E(m_k) = \mu_k(\theta_1, \theta_2, \ldots, \theta_m)$ and m_k is a consistent estimator of $\mu_k(\theta_1, \theta_2, \ldots, \theta_m)$. But since we are concerned with the behavior of the estimator of θ_i, $i = 1, 2, \ldots, m$, these properties are irrelevant. In the case of the estimator $\hat{\theta}_2 = \sum_{i=1}^{N} (X_i - \bar{X})^2/N$ of the parameter θ_2, in (2-5-2), the unbiasedness of m_2 as an estimator of $\mu_2(\theta_1, \theta_2)$ does not imply that θ_2 is an unbiased estimator θ_2. (This was shown in Section 2-2.)

In the final method to be considered, we use the fundamental interpretation of the quantity which we wish to estimate. That is, we try to develop a statistic as an estimator which has the same interpretation in the sample as the unknown quantity has in the population. Since there is no recipe for a general procedure, each estimator must be examined separately.

As an example of this type of procedure, consider the problem of estimating the unknown distribution function of a population, $F(x)$, by drawing a random sample $X_1, X_2, \ldots, X_N$. The fundamental interpretation of $F(x)$ is that it gives the probability that the random variable X will be less than or equal to x. A statistic which might have a similar interpretation in the sample of size N is

$$\hat{F}_N(x) = \frac{\text{number of } X_i \text{ in sample} \leq x}{N} \qquad (2\text{-}5\text{-}7)$$

since $\hat{\mathbf{F}}_N(x)$ is the proportion of sample values less than or equal to x. For large samples, proportions are approximately equal to probabilities, so the interpretations are similar. It can, in fact, be shown that $\hat{\mathbf{F}}_N(x)$ is a reasonable way to estimate $F(x)$; that is, the estimator $F_N(x)$ has some desirable properties. These properties are difficult to state in the terms defined because we are not estimating an unknown parameter but an unknown function. Similarly, for any particular sample size N, the estimator is a function. This type of partially specified probability model, where the unspecified elements are *not* unspecified parameters, is called a *non-parametric* model. Thus, estimation procedures applied to non-parametric models are called *non-parametric* methods of estimation.

Exercises

2–1. For the likelihood functions obtained in Exercise 1-4, find the maximum likelihood estimators of the parameters.

2–2. Verify that the estimators obtained in Exercise 2-1 are consistent.

2–3. Are the estimators obtaned in Exercise 2-1 unbiased?

2–4. For those estimators which are found to be unbiased in Exercise 2-3, determine if they are U. M. V. estimators.

2–5. For the likelihood functions obtained in Exercise 1-6, find the maximum likelihood estimators of the parameters.

2–6. Are the estimators obtained in Exercise 2-5 unbiased?

2–7. For those estimators which are found to be unbiased in Exercise 2-6 determine if they are U. M. V. estimators.

2–8. Place three pieces of paper—numbered 1, 2 and 3—in a hat. Without looking, select a piece of paper and record whether the number on the paper is odd or even, then replace it. Shake the hat after the paper is replaced and repeat the procedure five times. Define a partially specified probabilistic model describing this procedure. Determine an appropriate estimator of the unknown parameter in the model.

2–9. Repeat 25 times the experiment proposed in Exercise 2-5. For each experiment compute the estimator proposed in Exercise 2-8, then take the average of these estimators. Is the average value an intuitively better estimator than any of the original estimators?

Justify your answer in terms of the criteria for good estimators given in Section 2-2.

2–10. For the regression model

$$E(Y_{x_i}) = a + bx_i + cx_i^2 \qquad i = 1, 2, \ldots, N$$

determine the normal equations which must be solved to obtain least squares estimates of the parameters.

2–11. For the data of Problem 2-4-1, assume the regression model of Exercise 2-10 and find the estimator of the parameters a, b, c.

2–12. Some economic phenomena which are periodic can be represented by the regression model

$$E(Y_{x_i}) = a + b \sin \frac{2\pi x_i}{N} + c \cos \frac{2\pi x_i}{N}$$

where $x_i = 1, 2, \ldots kN$; k is an integer. Find the normal equations for this model.

2–13. In the model of Exercise 2-12, let $k = 4$ and $N = 3$. This would correspond to a model in which we observe the phenomena quarterly and there is a yearly periodic behavior. Let Y_{x_i} equal the quarterly values of woolen suits sold by a large clothing store chain. The observed values of Y_{x_i} are given in the table:

x_i	1	2	3	4	5	6	7	8	9	10	11	12
Y_{x_i}	14	29	62	34	18	38	70	29	10	27	58	24

Determine the least squares estimates for a, b, c.

chapter three

Hypothesis Testing and Confidence Interval Estimation

3–1. INTRODUCTION

In the last chapter, we considered the problem of estimating an unknown parameter based on the observations of a random sample. We
could restate this problem as that of selecting one parameter from the
usually infinite collection of possible parameters called the parameter
space. The problem of hypothesis testing is also a problem of selection.
In its simplest form, however, we shall consider it a problem of deciding
to which *one of two groups* does the unknown parameter belong.

   Problem 3-1-1. If we consider Problem 1-1-1 in a slightly different
manner we can formulate an hypothesis testing problem. Originally,

we wished to select a particular value of λ from the collection of $\lambda > 0$. Now, if the distributor is trying to determine whether or not he has sufficient capital to finance this venture, he might only be interested in knowing whether, on the average, he will have to stock fewer than 100 ranges or 100 ranges or more. (In the latter case, he would have to inquire about obtaining a bank loan; whereas, in the former case, his resources would be sufficient.)

The distributor is only concerned, then, with determining to which of two groups does the unknown parameter λ belong: one group consists of all λ between zero and one hundred and the other consists of all λ greater than or equal to 100.

In general, the hypothesis testing problem may be formulated: Suppose that a probability model specifies a group of probability density functions. We divide these functions into two groups; one group is given the name *null hypothesis*, denoted H_0, and the other group is given the name *alternative hypothesis*, denoted H_1. On the basis of a random sample, we must decide to which group the unknown density function belongs.

Definition 3-1-1. A null hypothesis or an alternative hypothesis is called a *simple* hypothesis if it consists of only one probability density function.

Definition 3-1-2. A null hypothesis or an alternative hypothesis is called a *composite* hypothesis if it consists of more than one probability density function.

We may now state Problem 3-1-1 as:

$$\text{Null hypothesis } H_0\colon p(x, \lambda) = \frac{\lambda^x e^{-\lambda}}{x!} \qquad 0 < \lambda < 100$$

$$\text{Alternative hypothesis } H_1\colon p(x, \lambda) = \frac{\lambda^x e^{-\lambda}}{x!} \qquad \lambda \geq 100 \qquad (3\text{-}1\text{-}1)$$

Here both the null hypothesis and the alternative hypothesis are composite. An alternative notation of (3-1-1) is:

$$\text{Null hypothesis } H_0\colon 0 < \lambda < 100$$

$$\text{Alternative hypothesis } H_1\colon \lambda \geq 100 \qquad (3\text{-}1\text{-}2)$$

Describing the two groups of functions by the appropriate range of a given parameter is sometimes useful since the selection of a group of functions is based on the selection of a group of parameters. The advantage of the formulation, in terms of density functions, is that it can be used equally well for parametric or non-parametric models.

To determine why this type of decision problem is called a problem of hypothesis testing, we must discuss a special type of decision problem, one in which the elements in the null hypothesis group are interpreted to represent the status quo, and the elements in the alternative hypothesis group to represent the alternative to the status quo. Consider the following:

Problem 3-1-2. A biologist is performing experiments with a new drug which he thinks will increase the average life expectancy of mice who have been injected with a certain type of cancer. He knows from past experience that the life expectancy of mice with or without this type of cancer is a normally distributed random variable having a mean of μ days and a standard deviation of one day. If the mice have the cancer, $\mu = 10$; if they do not, $\mu > 10$. The experiments are for determining if, in fact, the drug has the anticipated effect.

The biologist wishes to test a scientific hypothesis—that the new drug has a desirable effect on the life expectancy of mice with cancer. There are two possibilities to consider: the drug has no effect, or the drug has a beneficial effect. (We exclude the possibility that it has a harmful effect.) The former possibility is the null hypothesis since it leaves things as they were; the latter possibility is the alternative to the status quo and, therefore, the alternative hypothesis. In the probabilistic terms of Problem 3-1-2 we can formulate these hypotheses as

$$H_0: f(x) = \frac{1}{\sqrt{2\pi}} e^{-1/2(x-10)^2}$$

$$H_1: f(x) = \frac{1}{\sqrt{2\pi}} e^{-1/2(x-\mu)^2} \qquad \mu > 10$$

So we have a simple null hypothesis and a composite alternative hypothesis.

Although in the problem of the distributor it is not possible to give a completely analogous interpretation to the null and alternative hypotheses, as in the problem of the biologist, the terminology is still used. We could consider the null hypothesis $0 < \lambda < 100$ as the status quo since it means that the distributor will not have to negotiate a loan. The important factor in determining which group shall be called the null hypothesis and which shall be called the alternative hypothesis is the different types of errors which can occur. We make an error, which we will call a type I error, if we decide that the alternative hypothesis is true when the null hypotheses is true. We also make an error, a type II error, if we decide that the null hypothesis is true when the alternative hypothesis is true. Because the names null hypotheses and alternative hypotheses are so assigned to the groups of density functions, a type I error is the more serious of the two. Concerning the biologist, then, it is a more serious error to state that the new drug has a beneficial effect (H_1) when, in fact, it does not (H_0), than to state that the drug has no beneficial effect (H_0) when, in fact, it does (H_1).

At first, both errors might appear to be of equal gravity: a type I error could unjustifiably initiate a program of extensive research, at considerable expense; a type II error could mean that a great deal of time would be spent trying to develop an effective drug, when the drug in hand *is* effective and could be benefiting mankind. This, in fact, might seem even more serious than the type I error. However, deciding upon the null hypothesis is not an unequivocal statement that the alternative is not true. Acceptance of H_0 in this case only means that *the evidence does not indicate* that the drug has a beneficial effect. So the action taken after a type II error would be, simply, to check the evidence and make additional tests, which is a less costly action than in the case of a type I error, and the biologist would eventually discover the true state of affairs.

In the case of the distributor, a type I error would cause him to make a bank loan, unnecessarily, creating an additional expense over many years. A type II error, on the other hand, would cause him to attempt the new venture with insufficient capital. If we assume that the only consequence of this type of action would be that he would not meet demands until he could initiate a bank loan, and therefore decrease profits temporarily, then the type I error would be more serious.

Since there are only two possible decisions, we might have stated the different decisions in terms of the null hypothesis alone. That is, we either (a) accept the null hypothesis or (b) reject the null hypothesis. Then a type I error occurs if we reject the null hypothesis when it is true, and a type II error occurs if we accept the null hypothesis when it is false.

Our task is to develop procedures which will enable us, on the basis of a random sample of size N, to accept or reject the null hypothesis. The procedure which is used is to think of any set of N observations as a point in an N-dimensional space. Then, we need to define a region in N-dimensional space, called the *critical region*, such that: if the point falls in the critical region, we will reject the null hypothesis; if the point lies outside the critical region, we will accpet the null hypothesis. In two dimensions, we might define the critical region as the points inside the circle $x_1^2 + x_2^2 = 1$, given by the shaded area in Figure 3-1-1. Then if our observations were $x_1 = 1/2$, $x_2 = 3/4$, when plotted as a point in 2-dimensional space, it would lie within the critical region and we would reject the null hypothesis. Clearly, this graphical procedure would not be possible with an N larger than 3.

In order to develop an equivalent algebraic procedure, consider the two-dimensional space where the critical region is defined by the relations $(x_1 + x_2)/2 \geq 1/2$ and $(x_1 + x_2)/2 \leq -1/2$. The relation defining this region, the shaded area in Figure 3-1-2, can be stated in terms of the statistic $\bar{x}$, as $\bar{x} \geq 1/2$ and $\bar{x} \leq -1/2$. It is more usual to state the critical region

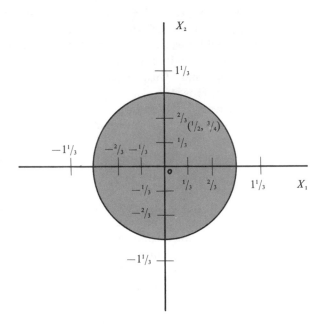

**FIGURE 3-1-1. Critical region inside the
circle $x_1^2 + x_2^2 = 1$**

in terms of a statistic and to verify algebraically whether or not a sample
point falls in the critical region, than to use a geometric interpretation.

The procedure for deciding between the null hypothesis and the alternative hypothesis follows: Decide, first, upon a critical region R. Then
take a random sample and determine by algebraic or geometric methods
if the sample observation point lies in the critical region. If the point lies
in the critical region, reject the null hypothesis. If it lies outside the critical
region, accept the null hypothesis. Such a procedure is called a *test of
hypothesis* based on the critical region R.

3–2. PROPERTIES OF TESTS OF HYPOTHESIS

Now we must establish some criteria to determine if a test of hypothesis
based on given critical region R is a good test. First let us consider the
size of the critical region R. Let $X_1, X_2, \ldots, X_N$ be a random sample of
size N from a population having a density function $f(x)$.

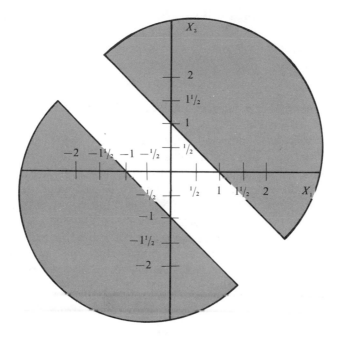

FIGURE 3-1-2. Critical region $= (x_1 + x_2)/2 \geq 1/2$
and $(x_1 + x_2)/2 \leq -1/2$

Definition 3-2-1. The critical region R is of size α if

$$P\{(X_1, X_2, \ldots, X_N) \in R \mid f(X) \in \mathrm{H}_0\} \leq \alpha$$

for all $f(x) \in \mathrm{H}_0$ and the equality holds for at least one density function belonging to H_0.

The interpretation of the size of the critical region is that it will set the upper limit on the probability with which a type I error will be made no matter which function belonging to the null hypothesis is true. The size, therefore, must always be between zero and one. Since, by convention, we have agreed that the type I error is the more serious error, we would usually like the size of the critical region to be small. It is emphasized that the size of the critical region does not refer to the volume of the geometric region R, but to Definition 3-2-1. A test of hypothesis performed using a critical region R of size α is called a *size α test*.

Next, let us consider the *power of a critical region*.

Definition 3-2-2. The critical region R has power β for accepting a density function $f(X)$ belonging to H_1 if

$$P\{(X_1, X_2, \ldots, X_N) \in R \mid f(X) \in H_1\} = \beta$$

The power of the region R will vary, depending which density function belonging to H_1 is being considered. The power of the critical region for rejecting the particular alternative can be expressed also as

$$\beta = 1 - P\{(X_1, X_2, \ldots, X_N) \in R \,|\, f(X) \in H_1\}$$
$$= 1 - P\{\text{type II error} \,|\, f(X) \in H_1\}$$

since the events that a point does or does not belong to R are mutually exclusive and exhaustive.

Using the concepts of size and power of a critical region, we can now describe a procedure for comparing various tests of hypothesis based on different critical regions. Comparisons are to be made only among critical regions having the same size α. The value of α is selected arbitrarily and is usually small; typical values are .05, .01. Of all regions of size α, we consider that which gives maximum power for all alternatives to be the best. Often there are two regions having size α, and neither will give the largest power for all alternatives. To handle this, we may introduce additional conditions, but they are still related to size and power. The concept of power is sometimes neglected in application since it can involve difficult computations. But that practice should not be carried over to cases where such computations are possible.

Here are two simple examples to illustrate these concepts. First, consider the following problem.

Problem 3-2-1. Suppose that we have 5 urns, each of which contains 4 balls (see Figure 3-2-1). Given one of the urns, we are asked to decide

	Urn 1	Urn 2	Urn 3	Urn 4	Urn 5
Red balls:	0	1	2	3	4
Black balls:	4	3	2	1	0

FIGURE 3-2-1.   Contents of urn for problem 3-2-1

if it is or is not Urn 3. And to help us to make our decision we are permitted to select at random one ball from the urn, replace it, and then select one more ball at random. It is assumed that we may not look into the urn, and that the only information we obtain about the contents of the urn is by noting the colors of the balls drawn.

To discuss this problem in the terminology of hypothesis testing, we must first establish a probability model for it. Let us define a random variable, $X^{(j)}$, which equals zero if a red ball is drawn from urn j, and equals one if a black ball is drawn from urn j. Since the balls are selected at random with replacement we have

$$P\{X^{(j)} = 0\} = p_j = (j-1)/4 \qquad j = 1, 2, 3, 4, 5$$
$$P\{X^{(j)} = 1\} = 1 - p_j \qquad\qquad j = 1, 2, 3, 4, 5$$

That is, the probability of a red ball on either draw from urn j is p_j; whereas $1 - p_j$ is the probability of drawing a black ball. Thus, for urn j we have a Bernoulli random variable with parameter p_j. An equivalent statement of the decision problem is that we wish to determine whether we should accept the null hypothesis or the alternative hypothesis, where we define:

Null hypothesis H_0: $P\{X = 0\} = 1/2$ $P\{X = 1\} = 1/2$
Alternative hypothesis H_1: $P\{X = 0\} = 0$ $P\{X = 1\} = 1$
$P\{X = 0\} = 1/4$ $P\{X = 1\} = 3/4$
$P\{X = 0\} = 3/4$ $P\{X = 1\} = 1/4$
$P\{X = 0\} = 1$ $P\{X = 1\} = 0$

The null hypothesis is simple and corresponds to the probability distribution of a Bernoulli random variable with the parameter p equal to 1/2; this is the distribution which would hold if we were selecting a ball at random from Urn 3. The alternative hypothesis is composite and consists of those probability distributions which would hold if we were selecting a ball at random from any of the other urns. Our decision will be based on a sample of size 2, which may have one of four outcomes: (0, 0), (0, 1), (1, 0), (1, 1), where we define X_1 as the outcome of the first sample, and X_2 as that of the second sample. Since a test of hypothesis is described by defining a critical region R, we will define three tests by defining three critical regions, $R_1 = \{(1, 0), (0, 1)\}$, $R_2 = \{(1, 1), (0, 0)\}$, and $R_3 = \{(0, 0), (0, 1)\}$, and determine which of these regions yields the best test. Intuitively R_1 would appear to be the least desirable because it rejects the null hypothesis when, in fact, the maximum likelihood estimate of p would be 1/2. R_2, on the other hand, rejects the null hypothesis when the maximum likelihood estimate of p is either zero or one.

The first step in a systematic investigation of these regions is to compute their size. For R_1 we have

$$P\{(X_1, X_2) \in R_1 | H_0\} = P\{X_1 = 1, X_2 = 0 | H_0\} + P\{X_1 = 0, X_2 = 1 | H_0\}$$
$$= (1 - p_3)p_3 + p_3(1 - p_3) = 1/2$$

since, under the condition that H_0 is true, $P\{X = 0\} = p_3 = P\{X = 1\} = 1 - p_3 = 1/2$. Similarly, we calculate that the size of the critical regions R_2 and R_3 are also 1/2 since the probability of any sample of size 2, given that H_0 is true, is 1/4. Had we selected a critical region with only one point, it would have size 1/4. But it is not possible to select a critical region with size α $1/4 < \alpha < 1/2$. This example illustrates that we may not always arbitrarily select a value of α and expect to create a region having that size.

In almost all problems where it is possible to construct one critical region of size α, it is usually possible to construct several. We must then use power considerations to choose between them. The power computations are usually more difficult because the alternative hypothesis is usually a composite hypothesis containing many probability distributions. In addition, in some problems, the alternatives may not be stated precisely; for example, Problem 3-2-1 might have stated that there were 5 urns, only one of which had 2 red balls and 2 black balls, and might then have asked us to decide if the urn presented to us had that composition. The alternative hypothesis could include many possibilities since we do not specify that all urns have four balls. To list all distributions belonging to the alternative hypothesis, we must consider urns with all possible combinations of colored balls, not only red and black, and with all possible numbers of balls. It is essential, therefore, in problem formulation to precisely state both the null hypothesis and the alternative hypothesis.

To compute the power of the region R_1, consider the probability distribution belonging to the alternative hypothesis that has p_j, $j = 1, 2, 4, 5$ as the probability of a red ball. We obtain

$$
\begin{aligned}
&P\{(X_1, X_2) \in R_1 | p_j \in H_1\} \\
&= P\{X_1 = 1, X_2 = 0 | p_j \in H_1\} + P\{X_1 = 0, X_2 = 1 | p_j \in H_1\} \\
&= (1 - p_j)p_j + p_j(1 - p_j) = 2p_j(1 - p_j) \qquad j = 1, 2, 4, 5
\end{aligned}
$$

Similarly, we could obtain the power of regions R_2 and R_3 for a particular alternative p_j. This is summarized in Figure 3-2-2.

Region R_1 can be eliminated from consideration because it has smaller power for all alternatives than R_2. The choice of a critical region now is narrowed to R_2 or R_3. Against alternatives such as p_1 and p_2, the region R_2 has greater power than R_3, but against alternative p_4, R_3 has greater power than R_2. In order to choose between these regions, we must invoke some additional criteria for selection.

Probability $(X_1, X_2) \in R_i$ given p_j

Critical Region	$p_1 = 0$	$p_2 = 1/4$	$p_3 = 1/2$	$p_4 = 3/4$	$p_5 = 1$
$R_1 = \{(1, 0), (0, 1)\}$	0	6/16	1/2	6/16	0
$R_2 = \{(1, 1), (0, 0)\}$	1	10/16	1/2	10/16	1
$R_3 = \{(0, 0), (0, 1)\}$	0	4/16	1/2	12/16	1

FIGURE 3-2-2. Power of critical regions for problem 3-2-1

Recall that the power against a particular member of the alternative hypothesis equals 1 minus the probability of a type II error. If we can specify for certain members of the alternative hypothesis that the probability of a type II error does not exceed a fixed probability r, then that specification may be used as a criterion for selection between various critical regions. This would be equivalent to a specification that the power for certain members of the alternative hypothesis would be greater than some fixed probability $\beta = 1 - r$. Since our computations in Figure 3-2-2 are in terms of power, we will use the last specification to choose between R_2 and R_3. Select $\beta = 7/16$, and require that for all members of the alternative hypothesis the power should be greater than β. From the second row in Figure 3-2-2, we know that R_2 satisfies this criterion, but from the third row, it is clear that R_3 does not. Therefore, R_2 is selected as the best region to make our decision. Note that had we selected some other value of β, for example $\beta = 11/16$, that criterion would be of no value in selecting between the regions.

The region R_1 is called an *inadmissible region* or, in terms of tests of hypothesis, the test corresponding to R_1 is an inadmissible test. In more general terms, we may define an inadmissible region as follows:

Definition 3-2-3. A region R of size α is an *inadmissible region* if there exists another region R' of size α whose power is at least as great as that of R for all density functions belonging to the alternative hypothesis with R' having greater power than R for one element of the alternative hypothesis. A region which is *not* inadmissible is said to be an *admissible region*.

We shall now consider a problem in which both the null hypothesis and the alternative hypothesis are composite. Let us define the two collections by the relations

$$H_0 : f(x, \theta) = \frac{\exp^{[-1/2\,[(x-\theta)^2]/2]}}{\sqrt{2\pi}\sqrt{2}} \qquad \theta \leq 0$$

$$H_1 : f(x, \theta) = \frac{\exp^{-1/2\,[(x-\theta)^2/2]}}{\sqrt{2\pi}\sqrt{2}} \qquad \theta > 0$$

The null hypothesis consists of all normal distributions* with variance 2 and non-positive mean, whereas the alternative hypothesis consists of normal distributions with variance 2 and positive mean. We will consider

---

*The normal distribution holds a prominent place in statistics because many probabilistic models assume that the observed phenomenon is a random variable having a normal distribution. The fact that an observable phenomenon is the aggregation of a large number of non-observable independent phenomena is usually the justification for the assumption that the observed phenomenon is a normally distributed random variable. This assumption is a consequence of the Central Limit Theorem. For this reason hypotheses concerning the normal distribution have been studied extensively and mathematical tables needed to perform the calculations for this type of example are readily available.

two types of critical regions for this problem. Defined in terms of the statistic $\bar{X} = (X_1 + X_2 + \ldots X_N)/N$, they have the form

$$R_1 = \{(X_1, X_2, \ldots, X_N) \text{ such that } \bar{X} \geq C_1\}$$
$$R_2 = \{(X_1, X_2, \ldots, X_N) \text{ such that } 0 \leq |\bar{X}| \leq C_2\}$$

For any given value of α, we shall first select C_1 and C_2 so that both critical regions have size α. Assume, for simplicity of calculation, that $N = 2$, from which it follows that $\bar{X}$ will be normally distributed with variance 1 and mean θ. We denote the probability density function of $\bar{X}$ by $g(\bar{X}, \theta)$. The value of θ will depend upon which element of the null hypothesis or the alternative hypothesis we assume to be the true density function of the sample values X_i, $i = 1, 2$.

Now we shall choose C_1 and C_2 so that both regions are of size $\alpha = .05$. Considering the density $f(X, 0)$ which belongs to the null hypothesis, we compute C_1 such that

$$P\{\bar{X} > C_1 | f(x, 0)\} = P\{\bar{x} > C_1 | g(\bar{x}, 0)|\}$$
$$= \int_{C_1}^{\infty} g(\bar{x}, 0) \, d\bar{x} = \int_{C_1}^{\infty} \frac{1}{\sqrt{2\pi}} e^{-(1/2)\bar{x}^2} \, d\bar{x} = .05 \quad (3\text{-}2\text{-}1)$$

From the tables of the area under the normal curve having mean 0 and variance 1, we obtain $C_1 = 1.645$. In order for R_1 to have size $\alpha = .05$, we must also show that

$$P\{\bar{X} > 1.645 | f(x, \theta), \theta < 0\} \leq \alpha \quad (3\text{-}2\text{-}2)$$

for all values of $\theta < 0$. To show that (3-2-2) holds, we note that

$$P\{\bar{X} > 1.645 | f(x, \theta), \theta < 0\} = P\{\bar{X} > 1.645 | g\bar{x}, \theta), \theta > 0\}$$
$$= \int_{1.645}^{\infty} g(\bar{x}, \theta) \, d\bar{x} = \int_{1.645}^{\infty} \frac{1}{\sqrt{2\pi}} e^{-1/2(\bar{x}-\theta)^2} \, d\bar{x} \quad (3\text{-}2\text{-}3)$$

By making a change of variable to the variable $z = \bar{x} - \theta$, we obtain

$$\int_{1.645}^{\infty} \frac{1}{\sqrt{2\pi}} e^{-1/2(\bar{x}-\theta)^2} \, d\bar{x} = \int_{1.645-\theta}^{\infty} \frac{1}{\sqrt{2\pi}} e^{-(1/2)z^2} \, dz$$
$$\leq \int_{1.645}^{\infty} \frac{1}{\sqrt{2\pi}} e^{-(1/2)z^2} \, dz = \alpha = .05 \quad (3\text{-}2\text{-}4)$$

since $\theta < 0$ and therefore $1.645 < 1.645 - \theta$.

Now, to find the constant C_2 which, in the same manner, will make R_2 of size α, consider the density $f(x, 0)$ and determine C_2 such that

$$P\{0 \leq |\bar{X}| \leq C_2 | f(x, 0)\} = P\{0 \leq |\bar{X}| \leq C_2 | g(\bar{x}, 0)\}$$
$$= \int_{-C_2}^{C_2} g(\bar{x}, 0) \, d\bar{x} = \int_{-C_2}^{C_2} \frac{1}{\sqrt{2\pi}} e^{-(1/2)\bar{x}^2} \, d\bar{x} \quad (3\text{-}2\text{-}5)$$

From the tables of the area under a normal curve having mean 0 and variance 1, we find that $C_2 \cong .066$. For R_2 to have size $\alpha = .05$ we must also show that

$$P\{0 \le |\bar{X}| \le .066 | f(X, \theta), \theta < 0\} \le \alpha \qquad (3\text{-}2\text{-}6)$$

for all values of $\theta < 0$. Equation (3-2-6) holds if we note that

$$P\{0 \le |\bar{X}| \le .066 | f(x, \theta), \theta < 0\} = P\{0 \le |\bar{X}| \le .066 | g(\bar{x}, \theta), \theta < 0\}$$

$$= \int_{-.066}^{.066} g(\bar{x}, \theta)\, d\bar{x} = \int_{-.066}^{.066} \frac{1}{\sqrt{2\pi}} e^{-1/2(\bar{x}-\theta)^2}\, d\bar{x} \qquad (3\text{-}2\text{-}7)$$

By changing the variable to $z = \bar{x} - \theta$, we obtain

$$\int_{-.066}^{.066} \frac{1}{\sqrt{2\pi}} e^{-1/2(\bar{x}-\theta)^2}\, d\bar{x} = \int_{-.066-\theta}^{.066-\theta} \frac{1}{\sqrt{2\pi}} e^{-(1/2)z^2}\, dz$$

$$= \int_{.066}^{.066-\theta} \frac{1}{\sqrt{2\pi}} e^{-(1/2)z^2}\, dz + \int_{-.066}^{.066} \frac{1}{\sqrt{2\pi}} e^{-(1/2)z^2}\, dz$$

$$- \int_{-.066}^{-.066-\theta} \frac{1}{\sqrt{2\pi}} e^{-(1/2)z^2}\, dz \qquad (3\text{-}2\text{-}8)$$

the sum of the first two integrals giving the area under the curve between $-.066$ and $.066 - \theta$, from which we subtract the third integral which gives the area under the curve between $-.066$ and $-.066 - \theta$. In both the first and third integrals in the last equality of (3-2-8), we integrate over an interval of length θ, but it can be shown that the first integral will always be less than the third integral for any $\theta < 0$. We may therefore conclude:

$$\int_{-.066}^{.066} \frac{1}{\sqrt{2\pi}} e^{-1/2(x-\theta)^2}\, d\bar{x} \le \alpha = .05 \qquad (3\text{-}2\text{-}9)$$

which shows that R_2 with $C_2 = .066$ is also a region of size α.

Since R_1 and R_2 are both regions of size α, we must consider the power against different densities belonging to the alternative hypothesis in order to choose between these regions. Let $f(x, \theta)$, $\theta > 0$ be an arbitrary density belonging to the alternative hypothesis. Having decided on this alternative, we compute the power of R_1, and

$$P\{\bar{X} > 1.645 | f(x, \theta), \theta > 0\} = P\{\bar{X} > 1.645 | f(\bar{x}, \theta), \theta > 0\}$$

$$= \int_{1.645}^{\infty} \frac{1}{\sqrt{2\pi}} e^{-1/2(x-\theta)^2}\, d\bar{x} = \int_{1.645-\theta}^{\infty} \frac{1}{\sqrt{2\pi}} e^{-(1/2)z^2}\, dz \qquad (3\text{-}2\text{-}10)$$

Since $\theta > 0$ we know that the power of the region R_1 is always greater than α for every number of the alternative hypothesis.

Considering the region R_2 and an arbitrary member of the alternative hypothesis $f(x, \theta)$, $\theta > 0$, the power of R_2 in deciding upon this alternative, is computed, finding that

$$P\{0 \le |\bar{X}| \le .066 | f(x, \theta), \theta > 0\}$$

$$= P\{0 \le |\bar{X}| \le .066 | g(x, \theta), \theta > 0\}$$

$$= \int_{-.066-\theta}^{-.066} \frac{1}{\sqrt{2\pi}} e^{-(1/2)z^2}\, dz + \int_{-.066}^{.066} \frac{1}{\sqrt{2\pi}} e^{-(1/2)z^2}\, dz$$

$$- \int_{.066-\theta}^{.066} \frac{1}{\sqrt{2\pi}} e^{-(1/2)z^2}\, dz \qquad (3\text{-}2\text{-}11)$$

Since $\theta > 0$, and the integrand in the last equality of (3-2-11) is symmetric about 0, it is possible to show that the first integral is less than the third integral. So we have established that the power against any density belonging to the alternative hypothesis is less than α, and that region R_2 is inadmissible since the power of R_1 against this same density is always greater than α. In addition to being preferred to R_2, the region R_1 is preferred to any other region of size α, and it is called a uniformly most powerful critical region.

Definition 3-2-4. A critical region R of size α is said to be *uniformly most powerful* (U. M. P.) if every other critical region R' of size α is inadmissible.

The U. M. P. critical region is, clearly, the most desirable type of region. But for most problems involving both a composite null hypothesis and a composite alternative hypothesis, a U. M. P. critical region does not exist. Thus, we shall next consider a method of determining if a given region is uniformly most powerful.

3-3. MOST POWERFUL TESTS—NEYMAN-PEARSON LEMMA

To determine the uniformly most powerful critical region by the methods already presented would require a large amount of computation, evaluating the power of all conceivable regions having the same size. Fortunately, in some cases, it is possible to determine if a given critical region is most powerful by use of a theorem called the Neyman-Pearson Lemma. Also, it is possible to use this theorem to construct critical regions which are most powerful. Since U. M. P. critical regions exist only for the simplest types of hypothesis testing problems, the application of this theorem is limited; it does illustrate, however, that general mathematical results can be used to determine critical regions with good properties. In the last section, we defined critical regions which were *intuitively* reasonable. Both mathematical and intuitive approaches are useful, but the latter requires verification that the proposed region has desirable power properties, whereas, in the mathematical approach, these are assured. Then, too, in some problems the intuitive approach may be the only approach possible.

We will now state the Neyman-Pearson Lemma in its simplest form. Let H_0 be a simple null hypothesis which consists of the density function $f(X_1\theta_0)$, and let H_1 be a simple alternative hypothesis which consists of the single density function $f(X_1\theta_1)$; Let $X_1, X_2, \ldots, X_N$ be a random sample of size N.

Theorem* (**Neyman-Pearson Lemma**). If a critical region R and a positive constant k exist such that

$$\frac{\prod_{i=1}^{N} f(x_i, \theta_0)}{\prod_{i=1}^{N} f(x_i, \theta_1)} \leq k \text{ if } (x_1, x_2, \ldots, x_N) \text{ belongs to } R$$

$$\frac{\prod_{i=1}^{N} f(x_i, \theta_0)}{\prod_{i=1}^{N} f(x_i, \theta_1)} > k \text{ if } (x_1, x_2, \ldots, x_N) \text{ does not belong to } R \qquad (3\text{-}3\text{-}1)$$

then R is a most powerful critical region with respect to the alternative hypothesis H_1. The size of R is determined by the value of k.

It is intuitively reasonable that the null hypothesis should be rejected if the ratio in (3-3-1) is "small" since this implies that the numerator—the likelihood under H_0—is small, relative to the denominator—the likelihood under H_1. A similar argument can show that if the ratio is large, the evidence indicates that the null hypothesis is more likely than the alternative hypothesis and should be accepted.

Although the theorem states a way to verify whether or not a critical region R is most powerful, it is possible by examining the ratio in (3-3-1) to determine how R must be defined so that the conditions of the theorem hold. To illustrate this procedure, examine the hypothesis-testing problem:

$$H_0: f(x, \theta_0) = \frac{1}{\sqrt{2\pi}} e^{-1/2(x-\theta_0)^2}$$

$$H_1: f(x, \theta_1) = \frac{1}{\sqrt{2\pi}} e^{-1/2(x-\theta_1)^2} \qquad (3\text{-}3\text{-}2)$$

Now, forming the ratio in (3-3-1), we obtain

$$\frac{\prod_{i=1}^{N} f(x_i, \theta_0)}{\prod_{i=1}^{N} f(x_i, \theta_1)} = \frac{\left(\frac{1}{\sqrt{2\pi}}\right)^N \exp -\frac{1}{2} \sum_{i=1}^{N} (x_i - \theta_0)^2}{\left(\frac{1}{\sqrt{2\pi}}\right)^N \exp -\frac{1}{2} \sum_{i=1}^{N} (x_i - \theta_1)^2}$$

$$= \exp\left\{ -\frac{1}{2}\left[\sum_{i=1}^{N}(x_i - \theta_0)^2 - \sum_{i=1}^{N}(x_i - \theta_1)^2\right]\right\}$$

$$= \exp\left\{ -\frac{N}{2}(\theta_0^2 - \theta_1^2) + (\theta_0 - \theta_1)N\bar{x}\right\}$$

$$= \exp\left\{ -\frac{N}{2}(\theta_0^2 - \theta_1^2)\right\} \exp\{(\theta_0 - \theta_1)N\bar{x}\} \qquad (3\text{-}3\text{-}3)$$

---

*We have assumed $f(x, \theta_0)$ and $f(x, \theta_1)$ have the same functional form and differ only in an unknown parameter. This is not necessary in the general formulation, but in applications, it is the usual case.

If we examine the last expression in (3-3-3), we see that it is of the form $Ce^{-(\theta_0-\theta_1)N\bar{x}}$ since $\exp\{-N/2(\theta_0^2 - \theta_1^2)\} = C$ is a positive constant. Now consider this expression in order to define R, such that

$$Ce^{-(\theta_0-\theta_1)N\bar{x}} \leq k \text{ if } (x_1, x_2, \ldots, x_N) \text{ belongs to } R$$
$$Ce^{-(\theta_0-\theta_1)N\bar{x}} > k \text{ if } (x_1, x_2, \ldots, x_N) \text{ does not belong to } R \qquad (3\text{-}3\text{-}4)$$

Note that $x_1, x_2, \ldots, x_N$ enter into (3-3-4) only through the function $\bar{x}$ and, therefore, we will define R in terms of $\bar{x}$. Assuming that $\theta_0 > \theta_1$, then $C \exp\{(\theta_0 - \theta_1)N\bar{x}\} \leq k$ if and only if $\log C + (\theta_0 - \theta_1)N\bar{x} \leq \log k$. This latter condition is equivalent to the condition that $\bar{x} \leq \log k - \log C/(\theta_0 - \theta_1)N$. Thus, if $\theta_0 < \theta_1$, we may define the critical region R as follows: R consists of all points $(x_1, x_2, \ldots, x_N)$ for which $\bar{x} \leq \log k - \log C/(\theta_0 - \theta_1)N$. From the method of defining R it follows that if $(x_1, x_2, \ldots, x_N)$ belongs to R, then $\bar{x} \leq \log k - \log C/(\theta_0 - \theta_1)N$ and

$$Ce^{-(\theta_0-\theta_1)N\bar{x}} \leq C \exp\frac{(\theta_0 - \theta_1)N(\log k - \log C)}{N(\theta_0 - \theta_1)}$$
$$= C \exp(\log k - \log C)$$
$$= \frac{Ce^{\log k}}{e^{\log C}} = k$$

which is the first condition of the Neyman-Pearson Lemma. It can easily be verified that the second condition of the theorem is also satisfied since if $(x_1, x_2, \ldots, x_N)$ does not belong to R, then $\bar{x} > \log k - \log C/(\theta_0 - \theta_1)N$, and

$$Ce^{-(\theta_0-\theta_1)N\bar{x}} > C \exp\frac{(\theta_0 - \theta_1)N(\log k - \log C)}{(\theta_0 - \theta_1)N}$$
$$= C \exp(\log k - \log C)$$
$$= \frac{Ce^{\log k}}{e^{\log C}} = k$$

By a similar argument, if $\theta_1 > \theta_0$, we can show that the most powerful critical region for this hypothesis testing problem is: R consists of all points $(x_1, x_2, \ldots, x_N)$ for which $\bar{x} \geq \log k - \log C/(\theta_0 - \theta_1)N$.

Once the form of the critical region has been determined, we must find the value of $K = \log k - \log C/(\theta_0 - \theta)N$ for which the region has a specified size α. Assuming that $\theta_1 < \theta_0$, to determine a region of the given form having size $\alpha = .05$, then we must find a value of K such that

$$P\{\bar{X} \leq K | H_0\} = .05 \qquad (3\text{-}3\text{-}5)$$

Under the null hypothesis $\bar{X}$ is normally distributed with mean θ_0 and variance $1/N$. To compute the probability given in (3-3-5) note that the random variable $Z = \sqrt{N}(\bar{X} - \theta_0)$ is normally distributed with mean zero and variance one. It is possible to obtain from tables that

$$P\{Z \leq -1.645 \,|\, H_0\} = .05$$

and therefore

$$P\{(\bar{X} - \theta_0)\sqrt{N} \leq -1.645\} = .05$$

So we obtain that $K = (-1.645/\sqrt{N}) + \theta_0$, and we say that we are able to test the given null hypothesis at the .05 significance level. (The significance level of a test is the size of the corresponding critical region.)

It was essential here, in determining the form of the critical region, to know whether $\theta_1 < \theta_0$ or $\theta_0 < \theta_1$. Generally it is true that the alternative hypothesis, rather than the null hypothesis, is the factor which determines the form of the critical region and, therefore, it should be specified precisely. A critical region which may be most powerful for one alternative hypothesis, may not be for a different alternative hypothesis. In the case of a composite alternative hypothesis, it is usually difficult to find a critical region which is most powerful for all possible members of the alternative hypothesis.

Here, we also have a situation where $\bar{X}$ is a sufficient statistic, in terms of which the critical region is defined. This is due to the fact that if a sufficient statistic exists, the ratio in (3-3-1) can be written:

$$\frac{\prod_{i=1}^{N} f(x_i, \theta_0)}{\prod_{i=1}^{N} f(x_i, \theta_1)} = \frac{h(x_1, x_2, \ldots, x_N)}{h(x_1, x_2, \ldots, x_N)} \cdot \frac{k(t, \theta_0)}{k(t, \theta_1)} = \frac{k(t, \theta_0)}{k(t, \theta_1)}$$

Thus, in a most powerful test, if a sufficient statistic exists, the critical region is defined in terms of that statistic.

3–4. LIKELIHOOD RATIO TESTS

Since it is seldom that a most powerful test of hypothesis exists for problems involving both a composite null hypothesis and a composite alternative hypothesis, the method we have so far considered of constructing tests has limited application. The likelihood ratio method, which we will cover next, is analogous to the method of maximum likelihood for estimation problems. For, like the maximum likelihood method of estimation, the tests of hypothesis obtained by the likehihood ratio method have good properties even though we cannot be assured that every likelihood ratio test will be good.* And many of the standard statistical test procedures can be developed by the likelihood ratio method.

---

*We have not defined what good properties of tests are, except for being most powerful, but these properties generally involve power as well as additional restrictions.

To apply the method, consider only problems where the null hypothesis and the alternative hypothesis may be stated in terms of the unknown parameters of the density function. Thus, the hypothesis testing problem

$$\text{H: } f(x, 0) = \frac{1}{\sqrt{2\pi}} e^{-x^2/2} \qquad\qquad -\infty < x < \infty$$

$$\text{H: } f(x, \theta) = \frac{1}{\sqrt{2\pi}} e^{-1/2(x-\theta)^2} \qquad -\infty < x < \infty$$
$$-\infty < \theta < \infty$$
$$\theta \neq 0 \qquad\qquad (3\text{-}4\text{-}1)$$

may be stated in terms of the unknown parameter θ of a normal density function with mean θ and variance 1:

$$\text{H}_0: \quad \theta = 0$$
$$\text{H}_1: \quad -\infty < \theta < \infty, \theta \neq 0 \qquad\qquad (3\text{-}4\text{-}2)$$

In general, we have a density function, $f(x, \theta_1, \theta_2, \ldots, \theta_m)$ and we wish to test the hypothesis

$$\text{H}_0: \quad (\theta_1, \theta_2, \ldots, \theta_m) \text{ belongs to } \Omega_0 \qquad\qquad (3\text{-}4\text{-}3)$$

against

$$\text{H}_1: \quad (\theta_1, \theta_2, \ldots, \theta_m) \text{ belongs to } \Omega_1 \qquad\qquad (3\text{-}4\text{-}4)$$

where Ω_0 and Ω_1 are collections of possible values for the parameters $(\theta_1, \theta_2, \ldots, \theta_m)$. In (3-4-2) we have $\Omega_0 = 0$ and $\Omega_1 = $ *all real numbers except zero*. The critical region for the hypothesis testing problem in (3-4-3) and (3-4-4), based on a sample of size N, is defined in terms of

$$\lambda = \frac{\displaystyle\max_{\Omega_0} \prod_{i=1}^{N} f(X_i, \theta_1, \theta_2, \ldots, \theta_m)}{\displaystyle\max_{\Omega_0 \cup \Omega_1} \prod_{i=1}^{N} f(X_i, \theta_1, \theta_2, \ldots, \theta_m)} \qquad\qquad (3\text{-}4\text{-}5)$$

called the likelihood ratio statistic. The numerator of this expression gives the maximum value of the likelihood function where we may select for the values of $(\theta_1, \theta_2, \ldots, \theta_m)$ only elements belonging to Ω_0; whereas the denominator gives the maximum value of the likelihood function where we may select for the values of $(\theta_1, \theta_2, \ldots, \theta_m)$ elements belonging to either Ω_0 or Ω_1. Since the denominator will always be larger than the numerator, the likelihood ratio will be ≤ 1 and ≥ 0. If the sample observations are consistent with some element belonging to the null hypothesis, then the maximum value that the likelihood function will attain when we restrict the selection of values of $(\theta_1, \theta_2, \ldots, \theta_m)$ to elements belonging to Ω_0 will not differ much from the maximum value attainable when we select values of $(\theta_1, \theta_2, \ldots, \theta_m)$ belonging to Ω_0 or Ω_1. Therefore, we should accept the null hypothesis if the likelihood ratio is close to 1, and reject the null hypothesis if it is not. The critical region then will be of the form

$$\text{Reject } H_0 \text{ if } 0 \leq \lambda \leq C$$
$$\text{Accept } H_0 \text{ if } C < \lambda \leq 1 \qquad (3\text{-}4\text{-}6)$$

where the constant C is chosen so that the critical region has the desired size.

It is sometimes more convenient to consider the statistic $L = -2 \log \lambda$. If $0 \leq \lambda \leq C$ then $-2 \log C < L$, so that the critical region, when we consider L rather than λ, will reject H_0 if $L > C'$. One reason for considering the statistic L is that for large values of N, if we assume the null hypothesis to be true, it is distributed approximately as a chi-square random variable, with the degrees of freedom equal to the difference between the number of unspecified parameters in the null and alternative hypotheses. We can then determine C' so that critical region is of any given size α. In many cases, it is possible to find the exact distribution of L, or of λ, so we can determine the appropriate constants without the use of this approximation.

Consider the hypothesis testing problem in (3-4-1) or, equivalently, in (3-4-2), and determine the likelihood ratio test based on a sample of size N. To compute the likelihood ratio, the choice of the parameter θ, which maximizes the likelihood function when we restrict our choice to values in Ω_0 will be $\theta = 0$ since Ω_0 only has the single element zero. To maximize the likelihood function when the choice of possible values of θ can be from Ω_0 or Ω_1—that is, $-\infty < \theta < \infty$—is exactly the same problem as in trying to find the maximum likelihood estimator of θ, from a sample of size N from a normal population with mean θ and variance 1. The appropriate estimator of θ was found to be $\theta = \bar{X}$. And we obtain the likelihood ratio λ to be

$$\lambda = \frac{\prod\limits_{i=1}^{N} \frac{1}{\sqrt{2\pi}} \exp -\frac{1}{2} X_i^2}{\prod\limits_{i=1}^{N} \frac{1}{\sqrt{2\pi}} \exp -\frac{1}{2}(X_i - \bar{X})^2}$$
$$= \exp -\frac{1}{2} \sum_{i=1}^{N} X_i^2 - \frac{1}{2} \sum_{i=1}^{N} (X_i - \bar{X})^2$$
$$= \exp -\frac{1}{2} N \bar{X}^2 \qquad (3\text{-}4\text{-}7)$$

To determine the critical region of size α, we must find a constant C, such that $P\{0 \leq \exp -\frac{1}{2}N\bar{X}^2 \leq C\} = \alpha$ when the null hypothesis is true, which requires finding the probability distribution of the statistic $\exp -\frac{1}{2}N\bar{X}^2$. If we consider the statistic $L = -2 \log \lambda = N\bar{X}^2$, then the critical region is of the form $N\bar{X}^2 \geq C'$. To define a critical region of size α, we must find a value of C' such that $P\{N\bar{X}^2 \geq C'\} = \alpha$ when the null hypothesis is true. The value of C' can be obtained from tables of the chi-square distribution since $Z = \sqrt{N}\,\bar{X}$ is a normal random variable with mean zero and variance 1 when H_0 is true; and therefore $Z^2 = N\bar{X}^2$ is a chi-square random variable with one degree of freedom.

3–5. CONFIDENCE INTERVALS

In the previous chapter we discussed the problem of estimating the unknown parameter of a probability density or mass function from observations taken at random. Thus, for a Poisson mass function with unknown parameter λ, we would estimate the value of λ as the mean of the sample values. If the mean happened to be 1.0, then that would be our estimate of λ. But suppose we decided to estimate λ as 1.0001 instead of 1.0—that is, our estimator would be the sample mean plus .0001. It would not make a considerable difference in the probability calculations (made by inserting the estimated value in the probability mass function). And although the modified estimator would not satisfy the desirable properties discussed, it would be *close* to satisfying these conditions. On the other hand, an estimator of a form which adds to the sample mean a value of 1,000 would make a considerable difference in the estimated value if the observed sample mean is small. So we conclude that in *some* cases it would be desirable to estimate an unknown parameter by a range or interval of values, rather than one specific value.

If we do use an interval of values as our estimate, this interval will be a *confidence interval*; for by giving such an estimate, we are stating that the unknown value of the parameter is *one of the values in this interval*. Generally we have a rule for constructing the confidence interval based on the outcome of the sample. Using that, we construct an interval of values, then state that the unknown parameter is one of those values. The confidence intervals constructed will be different from sample to sample, so sometimes our statement will be correct and other times it will not. The probability with which a particular rule of construction will yield correct statements of the type just given is called the *confidence coefficient* for the confidence interval. If an interval has confidence coefficient .95, we state that the rule for constructing confidence intervals will yield correct statements for 95% of the samples. For example:

Problem 3-5-1. Assume that there is an urn containing a red balls and $(4 - a)$ black balls. Two balls are selected from the urn with replacement. Give a confidence interval estimate for a, and find its confidence coefficient.

To give the estimate, we must propose a rule which defines the interval based on the outcome of the sample. Let $X_i = 1$ if the outcome of the ith sample is a red ball, and $X_i = 0$ if the outcome is a black ball; $i = 1, 2$. We denote the lower and upper limits of the interval by $L(X_1, X_2)$ and $U(X_1, X_2)$, respectively, which indicates that these values depend up on the sample outcomes. Now we propose a rule for constructing the confidence interval for Problem 3-5-1, by defining the lower and upper limit:

$$L(X_1, X_2) = 2(X_1 + X_2) - 1$$
$$U(X_1, X_2) = 2(X_1 + X_2) + 2 \qquad (3\text{-}5\text{-}1)$$

and state that the value of a is a number between $L(X_1, X_2)$ and $U(X_1, X_2)$, or equal to one of the limits.

To determine the confidence coefficient, which we associate with the confidence interval whose endpoints are given by (3-5-1), assume that there is an independent referee who knows the actual value of a. Specifically, now, assume that $a = 2$. (The referee can determine when the statement concerning the value of a is correct.) Since there are only four different outcomes of the sample, all possibilities are enumerated in Figure 3-5-1. The only sample outcome for which the rule will yield an

Sample Outcomes	$L(X_1, X_2)$	$U(X_1, X_2)$
$X_1 = 0, \; X_2 = 0$	-1	2
$X_1 = 1, \; X_2 = 0$	1	4
$X_1 = 0, \; X_2 = 1$	1	4
$X_1 = 1, \; X_2 = 1$	3	6

FIGURE 3-5-1.

incorrect statement will be if $X_1 = 1$ and $X_2 = 1$, and this has probability $1/4$ since we have assumed that $a = 2$ and sampling is with replacement. Therefore, the probability of a correct statement is $3/4$; that is, the confidence coefficient is $3/4$.

Of course, in any real problem, there is no independent referee to evaluate the probability that the statements will be correct. So we must act as the independent referee, by assuming that each of the possible values of a is true, and then evaluate the rule's performance in terms of the probability that the statements will be correct (see Figure 3-5-2). If $a = 1$,

True value of a	0	1	2	3	4
Probability of a correct statement	1	15/16	3/4	15/16	1

FIGURE 3-5-2.

from Figure 3-5-1, a wrong statement will be made if $X_1 = 1$ and $X_2 = 1$. Also, since $a = 1$, the probability that $X_i = 1$ is $1/4$, so the probability of a wrong decision is $1/16$. Because we cannot know the true value of a, we cannot give the exact performance of the rule; but we can say that the probability of making a correct statement will be greater than or equal to $3/4$. If we denote by $p(a)$ the probability of a correct statement as a function of a, then the more general definition of the confidence coefficient can be given as: min $p(a)$; $a = 0, 1, 2, 3, 4$

Proceeding to a more general statement of the concepts of interval estimation, let $f(X, \theta)$ be a density function, with one unknown parameter θ which has a value in the parameter space Ω. We define, for any random sample $X_1, X_2, \ldots, X_N$, two real valued functions of the observations denoted by $L(X_1, X_2, \ldots, X_N)$ and $U(X_1, X_2, \ldots, X_N)$. We then state that the unknown value of the parameter is a number in the interval of real numbers between and including $L(X_1, X_2, \ldots, X_N)$ and $U(X_1, X_2, \ldots, X_N)$. This is the *confidence interval*. For each value of $\theta \in \Omega$, the probability that some value in the confidence interval is that of the unknown parameter can be computed as a function of the value of $\theta \in \Omega$ we assume to be true. These values will be denoted by $p(\theta)$; the confidence coefficient for the interval is defined as $\min_{\theta \in \Omega} p(\theta) = 1 - \alpha$. The interpretation of the procedure of confidence interval estimation is that in repeated applications in many samples, the proportion of correct statements (that some value in the confidence interval is the correct value of the parameter) will be greater than $1 - \alpha$.

If the unknown parameter is the quantity of interest in a problem, then interval estimation is a more appropriate method than point estimation since we are given a range of values. However, if we wish to use the estimated value of the parameter as an intermediate result, to be substituted into an equation to obtain a final result, the question is do we want for that final result a range of possible values or a single value that is, which method is appropriate for a given problem? It is emphasized that no special importance is given to values near the center of the confidence interval as opposed to those near the ends.

The criteria for selecting the better method of constructing a confidence interval is based, first, on the concept of the confidence coefficient. We arbitrarily select a value of $1 - \alpha$, and consider all methods of constructing confidence intervals which give the desired confidence coefficient. Since the construction of confidence intervals requires the definition of two functions, $L(X_1, X_2, \ldots, X_N)$ and $U(X_1, X_2, \ldots, X_N)$, we will use these functions to select one of the several methods. We define as the *length of a confidence interval* the expected value $U(X_1, X_2, \ldots, X_N)$, —

$L(X_1, X_2, \ldots, X_N)$, and choose among the intervals with the desired confidence coefficient the one with the shortest length.

The criteria for selecting the best rule for construction of confidence intervals is similar to the criteria for construction of a good critical region. To construct a critical region, we arbitrarily select a size α for the critical region; and, in the construction of confidence intervals, we arbitrarily select a confidence coefficient $1 - \alpha$. For all critical regions of size α, we then choose the one with greatest power; for all confidence intervals with confidence coefficient $1 - \alpha$, we select the one with shortest length. This relationship can be carried even further, using the methods for constructing tests of hypothesis to construct confidence intervals. To illustrate the procedure, we will consider the problem of constructing a confidence interval with confidence coefficient $1 - \alpha = .95$ for the unknown mean θ of a normal distribution with variance 1.

First, however, consider the problem of constructing a critical region of size $\alpha = .05$ to test:

$$H_0: f(x, \theta_0) = \frac{1}{\sqrt{2\pi}} e^{-1/2 [(x-\theta_0)^2]}$$

$$H_1: f(x, \theta) = \frac{1}{\sqrt{2\pi}} e^{-1/2 [(x-\theta)^2]} \qquad -\infty < \theta < \infty$$
$$\theta \neq \theta_0 \qquad \text{(3-5-2)}$$

By the likelihood ratio method we can obtain a critical region of the form where we reject the null hypothesis if $N(\bar{X} - \theta_0)^2 \geq K$. This region is equivalent to that which rejects the null hypothesis if and only if $\sqrt{N}(\bar{X} - \theta_0) \geq \sqrt{K}$ or $\sqrt{N}(\bar{X} - \theta_0) \leq -\sqrt{K}$. Therefore, the probability of rejecting H_0 when it is true is given by

$$P\{\sqrt{N}(\bar{X} - \theta_0) \geq \sqrt{K} | H_0\} + P\{\sqrt{N}(\bar{X} - \theta_0) \leq -\sqrt{K} | H_0\} \quad \text{(3-5-3)}$$

Since $\sqrt{N}(\bar{X} - \theta_0)$ is normally distributed with mean 0 and variance 1, we may obtain from tables of the area under the normal curve that if we select $\sqrt{K} = 1.96$, the probability given by (3-5-3) will equal .05; that is, the critical region will have size $\alpha = .05$.

Instead of focusing our attention on the critical region, we can consider those points which fall outside the critical region, which we will call the *acceptance region* since if a sample points falls in this region we will accept the null hypothesis. For the problem under consideration, the acceptance region can be defined as all points such that $-1.96 \leq N(\bar{X} - \theta_0) \leq 1.96$ or, equivalently, all points such that $(-1.96)/\sqrt{N} + \theta_0 \leq \bar{X} \leq (1.96)/\sqrt{N} + \theta_0$. In order that the null hypothesis be accepted, the latter formulation of the acceptance region states that $\bar{X}$ must satisfy the two inequalities, $-1.96/\sqrt{N} + \theta_0 \geq \bar{X}$ and $\bar{X} \leq 1.96/\sqrt{N} + \theta_0$ or, equivalantly, $\bar{X} + 1.96/\sqrt{N} \leq \theta_0$ and $\bar{X} - 1.96/\sqrt{N} \leq \theta_0$. If, in our rule for forming confidence intervals, we now use $L(X_1, X_2, \ldots, X_N) = \bar{X} - 1.96$ $/\sqrt{N}$ and $U(X_1, X_2, \ldots, X_N) = \bar{X} + 1.96/\sqrt{N}$, we will have a method of constructing a confidence interval with confidence coefficient $1 - \alpha = .95$. To show this, it is sufficient that for any fixed value of θ:

$$P\{U(X_1, X_2, \ldots, X_N) \geq \theta \text{ and } L(X_1, X_2, \ldots, X_N) \leq \theta \,|\, \theta\} = 1 - \alpha$$

$$(3\text{-}5\text{-}3)$$

Substituting the special functions $L(X_1, X_2, \ldots, X_N)$ and $U(X_1, X_2, \ldots, X_N)$ into (3-5-3), we obtain

$$P\{\bar{X} + 1.96/\sqrt{N} > \theta \text{ and } \bar{X} - 1.96/\sqrt{N} \leq \theta \,|\, \theta\}$$
$$= P\{\bar{X} - \theta \geq -1.96/\sqrt{N} \text{ and } \bar{X} - \theta \leq 1.96/\sqrt{N} \,|\, \theta\}$$
$$= P\{-1.96 \leq \sqrt{N}(\bar{X} - \theta) \leq 1.96 \,|\, \theta\} = .95 = 1 - \alpha \quad (3\text{-}5\text{-}4)$$

since, under the condition that θ is the true parameter value, $\sqrt{N}(\bar{X} - \theta)$ is a normal random variable with mean 0 and variance 1.

In general, if we have a critical region which is used to test a simple hypothesis against a composite alternative hypothesis, where the members of the alternative hypothesis group consist of all parameter values in the parameter space, it is possible to use the acceptance region to define the functions $L(X_1, X, _2 \ldots X_N)$ and $U(X_1, X_2, \ldots, X_N)$.

3–6. FURTHER APPLICATION OF HYPOTHESIS TESTING

In this section we shall consider some additional problems to which we can apply the principles of hypothesis testing. Because the mathematical details needed to precisely formulate and develop these procedures are more complex, they will be omitted. But an explanation will be made, where applicable, of how the test procedure was developed from the likelihood ratio statistic.

Problem 3-6-1. Assume that the length of life of a transistor is a normal random variable with mean μ and variance σ^2, where μ and σ^2 are unknown (since it is usually difficult to know the variance without knowing the mean). The manufacturer of these transistors would like to test N transistors until they fail, and use the results of the test to establish that the mean life μ equals a specified value μ_0—for example, $\mu_0 = 1000$ hours.

We can formulate this:

$$H_0: f(x, \mu_0, \sigma^2) = \frac{1}{\sqrt{2\pi}\sigma} e^{-(1/2\sigma^2)(x-\mu_0)^2} \qquad \sigma^2 > 0$$

$$H_1: f(x, \mu, \sigma^2) = \frac{1}{\sqrt{2\pi}\sigma} e^{-(1/2\sigma^2)(x-\mu)^2} \qquad -\infty < \mu < \infty$$
$$\mu \neq \mu_0$$
$$\sigma^2 > 0 \qquad (3\text{-}6\text{-}1)$$

Thus, we have a composite null hypothesis and a composite alternative hypothesis. By applying the methods of Section 3-4, we obtain the likelihood ratio statistic based on a random sample of size N:

$$\lambda = \left[\frac{\sum_{i=1}^{N} (X_i - \bar{X})^2}{\sum_{i=1}^{N} (X_i - \mu_0)^2} \right]^{N/2} = \left[\frac{1}{1 + \left[N(\bar{X} - \mu_0)^2 / \sum_{i=1}^{N} (X_i - \bar{X})^2 \right]} \right]^{N/2} \qquad (3\text{-}6\text{-}2)$$

since $\sum_{i=1}^{N} (X_i - \mu_0)^2 = \sum_{i=1}^{N} (X_i - \bar{X})^2 + N(\bar{X} - \mu_0)^2$. The critical region for this test rejects the null hypothesis if λ is small, which will occur if and only if the quantity $N(\bar{X} - \mu_0)^2 / \sum_{i=1}^{N} (X_i - \bar{X})^2$ is large. Therefore, we state the critical region in terms of that statistic:

$$\text{Reject if } N(\bar{X} - \mu_0)^2 / \sum_{i=1}^{N} (X_i - \bar{X}) > k \qquad (3\text{-}6\text{-}3)$$

The statistic here differs from a statistic having an F distribution with 1 and $N - 1$ degrees of freedom when H_0 is true by a factor of $N - 1$, so that (3-6-3) might be restated:

$$\text{Reject if } N(N - 1)(\bar{X} - \mu_0)^2 / \sum_{i=1}^{N} (X_i - \bar{X})^2 > k' \qquad (3\text{-}6\text{-}4)$$

We may, therefore, use the tables of the F distribution to determine k' to give the critical region any desired size α. To compute the power of this test for any alternative $\mu \neq \mu_0$ special tables would be required, so power computations for the problems in this section will not be considered.

An alternative way of stating (3-6-4) would be in terms of the requirement of the statistic given in (3-6-4) as follows:

$$\text{Reject if } \sqrt{N(N - 1)} |\bar{X} - \mu_0| \left/ \sqrt{\sum_{i=1}^{N} (X_1 - \bar{X})^2} \right. > \sqrt{k'} \qquad (3\text{-}6\text{-}5)$$

The statistic given (3-6-5) has a t distribution with $N - 1$ degrees of freedom when H_0 is true and it is this statistic which is usually used to test the hypothesis stated in (3-6-1). The constant k' which gives any desired size α can be obtained from tables of the t distribution.

In some problems the mean μ of the normal distribution may be less important than the variance σ^2. Consider the following problem:

Problem 3-6-2. Assume that a customer purchasing the transistors considered in Problem 3-6-1 is going to use 100 of them in manufacturing a subsystem of a complex and expensive piece of electronic equipment. If one of the transistors fails the equipment fails, causing considerable financial loss. It is easy however, to replace the subsystem before it fails. So the consumer specifies that he wants the transistors to have any reasonable value for μ, but insists that $\sigma^2 = \sigma_0^2$ of a specified value, say $\sigma_0^2 = 1$. The reason for this specification is to be sure that life expectancy of the transistors will be very close to μ hours. It would then be necessary to replace the subsystem every μ hours.

We may now formulate this problem in the following form:

$$H_0: f(x, \mu, \sigma_0^2) = \frac{1}{\sqrt{2\pi}\sigma_0} e^{-(1/2\sigma_0^2)(x-\mu)^2} \qquad -\infty < \mu < \infty$$

$$H_1: f(x, \mu, \sigma^2) = \frac{1}{\sqrt{2\pi}\sigma} e^{-(1/2\sigma^2)(x-\mu)^2} \qquad -\infty > \mu > \infty$$
$$\sigma^2 \neq \sigma_0^2, \sigma^2 > 0 \quad (3\text{-}6\text{-}6)$$

The likelihood ratio statistic based on a random sample of size N can be shown to be

$$\lambda = \left(\frac{\omega}{N}\right)^{N/2} e^{-(1/2)(\omega-N)} \qquad\qquad (3\text{-}6\text{-}7)$$

where

$$\omega = \sum_{i=1}^{N} (X_i - \bar{X})^2/\sigma_0^2 \qquad\qquad (3\text{-}6\text{-}8)$$

The critical region used to test the null hypothesis, given in (3-6-6), will be reject if $0 \leq \lambda < c$. To determine a value of c which will give the critical region size α it is necessary to find the probability distribution of λ in order to find a value of c such that $P\{0 \leq \lambda < c\} = \alpha$. To avoid this difficult task we can try to define the critical region in terms of the statistic ω. That is, we wish to determine what values of ω will make λ smaller than c. It can be shown that $0 \leq \lambda < c$ when and only when $0 < \omega < a$ or $b < \omega < \infty$ where

$$c = \left(\frac{a}{N}\right)^{N/2} e^{-(1/2)(a-N)} = \left(\frac{b}{N}\right)^{N/2} e^{-(1/2)(b-N)} \qquad (3\text{-}6\text{-}9)$$

Therefore the form of the critical region to test this null hypothesis in terms of ω is:

$$\text{Reject if } 0 < \omega < a \text{ or if } b < \omega < \infty \qquad\qquad (3\text{-}6\text{-}10)$$

where a and b must satisfy the last equality of (3-6-9).

In practice, if we wish to construct a critical region of size α, we choose a and b such that

$$P\{0 < \omega < a\} = P\{b < \omega < \infty\} = \frac{\alpha}{2} \qquad (3\text{-}6\text{-}11)$$

which can easily be obtained from tables of the X^2 distribution since ω has a X^2 distribution with $n - 1$ degrees of freedom when H_0 is true. The values of a and b, selected by using (3-6-11), will not satisfy the second equality in (3-6-9). Therefore, this is not strictly the likelihood ratio test, but it is a close approximation to it, and is the one usually used. To obtain the likelihood ratio test, we would have to find values of a and b such that:

$$P\{0 < \omega < a\} + P\{b < \omega < \infty\} = \alpha$$

$$\left(\frac{a}{N}\right)^{N/2} e^{-(1/2)(a-N)} = \left(\frac{b}{N}\right)^{N/2} e^{-(1/2)(b-N)} \qquad (3\text{-}6\text{-}12)$$

Until now, we have considered only problems where a random sample is taken from a single population. The concepts developed can be extended to the case where we select a random sample from more than one population. The purpose of this sampling procedure is to make a comparison between certain properties of the two populations. This approach is illustrated in the next two problems.

Problem 3-6-3. The manufacturer of transistors wishes to determine if his competitor is producing transistors with the same average length of life. To determine if this is true the manufacturer purchases M transistors from his competitor which we assume to be a random sample from a population of transistors where length of life is a normal random variable with mean μ_y and variance σ_y^2. He also selects N of his own transistors which have a length of life which is a normal random variable with mean μ_x and variance σ_x^2. He then tests the $N + M$ transistors until they fail and based upon this information about length of life he would like to decide whether or not $\mu_x = \mu_y$ where no value μ_x and μ_y is specified.

Let us define $X_1, X_2, \ldots, X_N$ to be the lengths of life if the manufacturer's own transistors and $Y_1, Y_2, \ldots, Y_M$ to be the lengths of life of the competitor's transistors in the test. We will assume in this problem that $\sigma_x^2 = \sigma_y^2 = \sigma^2$. The hypothesis testing problem may be stated as follows:

$$H_0: [f(x, \mu_x, \sigma^2), f(y, \mu_y, \sigma^2)]$$
$$f(x, \mu_x, \sigma^2) = f(y, \mu_y, \sigma^2) \qquad \mu_x = \mu_y$$
$$-\infty < \mu_x < \infty$$
$$-\infty < \mu_y < \infty \qquad \sigma^2 > 0$$

$$H_1: [f(x, \mu_x, \sigma^2), f(y, \mu_y, \sigma^2)]$$
$$f(x, \mu_x, \sigma^2) \neq f(y, \mu_y, \sigma^2) \qquad \mu_x \neq \mu_y$$
$$-\infty < \mu_x < \infty$$
$$-\infty < \mu_y < \infty \qquad \sigma^2 > 0 \qquad (3\text{-}6\text{-}13)$$

where

$$f(x, \mu_x, \sigma^2) = \frac{1}{\sqrt{2\pi}\sigma} e^{-(1/2\sigma^2)(x-\mu_x)^2}$$

$$f(y, \mu_y, \sigma^2) = \frac{1}{\sqrt{2\pi}\sigma} e^{-(1/2\sigma^2)(y-\mu_y)^2}$$

Thus, H_0 consists of all pairs of density functions of the random variables X and Y that are equal. The alternative hypothesis consists of all pairs that are not equal. This is somewhat different from problems in which we were only concerned with one population, where the null hypothesis was only a collection of density functions rather than a collection of *pairs* of density functions. The same principles used for a single population can be applied here if we assume that the different populations behave independently of each other.

The likelihood ratio statistic for this problem can be written:

$$\lambda = \left[\frac{1}{1 + \dfrac{\dfrac{MN}{M+N}(\bar{X} - \bar{Y})^2}{\sum\limits_{i=1}^{N}(X_i - \bar{X})^2 + \sum\limits_{i=1}^{M}(Y_j - \bar{Y})^2}} \right]^{(M+N)/2} \tag{3-6-14}$$

If we define the statistic

$$t = \frac{\sqrt{MN/(M+N)}\,(\bar{X} - \bar{Y})}{\sqrt{\sum\limits_{i=1}^{N}(X_i - \bar{X})^2 + \sum\limits_{j=1}^{M}(Y_j - \bar{Y})^2/(M+N-2)}} \tag{3-6-15}$$

then we can rewrite (3-6-14) as

$$\lambda = \left[\frac{1}{1 + t^2/(M+N-2)} \right]^{(M+N)/2} \tag{3-6-16}$$

Since the statistic defined in (3-6-15) has the t distribution when H_0 is true, it is desirable to define the critical region in terms of this statistic to avoid finding the distribution of λ. The critical region based upon λ rejects the null hypothesis when λ is small. This is equivalent to rejecting the null hypothesis if t^2 is large; but in order for t^2 to be large, t must be either a large positive number or a large negative number. We may state the critical region to test the null hypothesis as

$$\text{Reject if } t < -k \text{ or if } t > k \tag{3-6-17}$$

where k is selected to give the desired size α.

Problem 3-6-4. Assume that the consumer of transitors (in Problem 3-6-2) has been using transistors produced by a particular company. Another manufacturer offers him what he claims to be a transistor with the same small variability in length of life at a lower cost. In order to verify this statement, the consumer takes a random sample of size N from the old manufacturer and a random sample of size M from the new manufacturer. He tests the transistors for length of life which, in the first case, is normally distributed with mean μ_x and variance σ_x^2 and, in the second case, is normally distributed with mean μ_y and variance σ_y^2. On the basis of the test data, the consumer would like to determine if $\sigma_x^2 = \sigma_y^2$.

Using the notation developed in Problem 3-6-3 we may state this hypothesis testing problem as

$$H_0: [f(x, \mu_x, \sigma_x^2), f(y, \mu_y, \sigma_y^2)] \qquad -\infty < \mu_x < \infty$$
$$\sigma_x^2 = \sigma_y^2 \qquad -\infty < \mu_y < \infty$$
$$\sigma_x^2 \geq 0, \sigma_y^2 \geq 0$$
$$H_1: [f(x, \mu_x, \sigma_x^2), f(y, \mu_y, \sigma_y^2)] \qquad -\infty < \mu_x < \infty$$
$$\sigma_x^2 \neq \sigma_y^2 \qquad -\infty < \mu_y < \infty$$
$$\sigma_x^2 \geq 0, \sigma_y^2 \geq 0 \qquad (3\text{-}6\text{-}18)$$

where

$$f(x, \mu_x, \sigma_x^2) - \frac{1}{2\pi\sigma_x} \exp -\frac{1}{2\sigma_x^2}(x - \mu_x)^2$$

$$f(x, \mu_y, \sigma_y^2) = \frac{1}{2\pi\sigma_y} \exp -\frac{1}{2\sigma_y^2}(y - \mu_y)^2$$

Thus, the null hypothesis consists of all pairs of density functions with the same variance; the alternative hypothesis consists of all pairs of normal density functions with different variances. The likelihood ratio statistic, which can be developed to test this null hypothesis against this alternative hypothesis, is given by:

$$\lambda = \frac{(M + N)^{(M+N)/2}\left(\frac{N-1}{M-1}F\right)^{N/2}}{M^{M/2}N^{N/2}\left(1 + \frac{N-1}{M-1}F\right)^{(M+N)/2}} \qquad (3\text{-}6\text{-}19)$$

where

$$F = \frac{(M-1)\sum_{i=1}^{N}(X_i - \bar{X})^2}{(N-1)\sum_{j=1}^{M}(Y_j - \bar{Y})^2} \qquad (3\text{-}6\text{-}20)$$

When the null hypothesis is true, the statistic F has an F distribution with $N - 1$ and $M - 1$ degrees of freedom, and it is desirable to state the critical region in terms of this statistic. It can be shown that $0 \leq \lambda < c$ when and only when $0 \leq F < a$ or $b < F < \infty$, where a and b are such that substitution of these values for F, in (3-6-19), will make that expression equal to c. The critical region is stated in terms of F:

$$\text{Reject if } 0 \leq F < a \text{ or if } b < F < \infty \qquad (3\text{-}6\text{-}21)$$

To compute the values of a and b which will yield a critical region of size α, we use the relation:

$$P\{0 \leq F < a\} = P\{b < F < \infty\} = \frac{\alpha}{2} \qquad (3\text{-}6\text{-}22)$$

without regard to the restriction imposed by (3-6-19). Thus, the critical region of the form in (3-6-21), where a and b are determined by (3-6-22), is only a close approximation to the likelihood ratio test. But this region is the one used in practice since the values of a and b satisfying (3-6-22) can easily be obtained from tables of the F distribution.

Although the likelihood ratio method of constructing tests of hypotheses yields tests with good properties for many problems, it does not always yield the most useful test. In the next problem, the method given will lead to a test which can be improved upon.

Problem 3-6-5. A soap manufacturer wishes to determine if there is any relationship between a person's income and the type of soap which he buys. If there is, advertising policies may be formulated to make use of this. To find out whether or not such a relationship exists, a random sample of size N is taken. For each person in the sample, his income and the type of soap he most often buys are determined.

To solve this, we first must precisely formulate the probabilistic model to be considered. Assume that there are I mutually exclusive and exhaustive income groups, and J mutually exclusive and exhaustive types of soap. Each individual, then, can be classified as belonging to exactly one income group and using one type of soap most often. We define A_i $i = 1, 2, \ldots, I$ as the event that the person belongs to the income group numbered i, and B_j $j = 1, 2, \ldots, J$ as the event that the person most buys the soap of type j. The probability of the joint occurrence of the events A_i and B_j—that is, that the person belongs to group i and buys soap j—will be denoted by p_{ij}. We can display these probabilities, in tabular form, as follows:

	B_1	B_2	$\ldots$	B_j	$\ldots$	B_J	
A_1	p_{11}	p_{12}	$\ldots$	p_{1j}	$\ldots$	p_{1J}	q_1
A_2	p_{21}	p_{22}	$\ldots$	p_{2j}	$\ldots$	p_{2J}	q_2
.	.	.		.		.	.
.	.	.		.		.	.
.	.	.		.		.	.
A_i	p_{i1}	p_{12}	$\ldots$	p_{ij}	$\ldots$	p_{iJ}	q_i
.	.	.		.		.	.
.	.	.		.		.	.
.	.	.		.		.	.
A_I	p_{I1}	p_{I2}	$\ldots$	p_{Ij}	$\ldots$	p_{IJ}	q_I
	r_1	r_2	$\ldots$	r_j	$\ldots$	r_J	1

FIGURE 3-6-1. Probabilities for problem 3-6-5

In addition, it follows that:

$$P(A_i) = \sum_{j=1}^{J} P(A_i \cap B_j) = \sum_{j=1}^{J} p_{ij} = q_i; i = 1, 2, \ldots, I$$

$$P(B_j) = \sum_{i=1}^{I} P(A_i \cap B_j) = \sum_{i=1}^{I} p_{ij} = r_j; j = 1, 2, \ldots, J \quad (3\text{-}6\text{-}23)$$

(These quantities are presented in the margin of Figure 3-6-1.) The interpretation of probability p_{ij} is that, in the population, it is the proportion of people in income group i who also buy most of soap type j. The probabilistic statement that there is no relationship between income and the type of soap bought is:

$$P(A_i \cap B_j) - P(A_i)P(B_j) \qquad \begin{aligned} i &= 1, 2, \ldots, I \\ j &= 1, 2, \ldots, J \end{aligned}$$

or

$$p_{ij} = q_i r_j \qquad \begin{aligned} i &= 1, 2, \ldots, I \\ j &= 1, 2, \ldots, J \end{aligned}$$

We can now formulate Problem 3-6-5 as a hypothesis testing problem:

$$\begin{aligned} \mathrm{H}_0\colon\ & p_{ij} = q_i r_j & i &= 1, 2, \ldots, I \\ & & j &= 1, 2, \ldots, J \\ \mathrm{H}_1\colon\ & p_{ij} \neq q_i r_j & i &= 1, 2, \ldots, I \\ & & j &= 1, 2, \ldots, J \end{aligned}$$

where q_i and r_j are defined in (3-6-23). The null hypothesis and the alternative hypothesis are both composite. An element in the null hypothesis group is any collection of IJ non-negative numbers which sum to one and satisfy the condition in H_0. Similarly an element in the alternative hypothesis group is any collection of IJ non-negative numbers which sum to one and do not satisfy $p_{ij} = q_i r_j$.

It is possible to present the information obtained from the sample of size N as follows:

	B_1	B_2	$\ldots$	B_j	$\ldots$	B_J	
A_1	n_{11}	n_{12}	$\ldots$	n_{1j}	$\ldots$	n_{1J}	$n_{1.}$
A_2	n_{21}	n_{22}	$\ldots$	n_{2j}	$\ldots$	n_{2J}	$n_{2.}$
$\cdot$	$\cdot$	$\cdot$		$\cdot$		$\cdot$	$\cdot$
$\cdot$	$\cdot$	$\cdot$		$\cdot$		$\cdot$	$\cdot$
$\cdot$	$\cdot$	$\cdot$		$\cdot$		$\cdot$	$\cdot$
A_i	n_{i1}	n_{i2}	$\ldots$	n_{ij}	$\ldots$	n_{iJ}	$n_{i.}$
$\cdot$	$\cdot$	$\cdot$		$\cdot$		$\cdot$	$\cdot$
$\cdot$	$\cdot$	$\cdot$		$\cdot$		$\cdot$	$\cdot$
$\cdot$	$\cdot$	$\cdot$		$\cdot$		$\cdot$	$\cdot$
A_I	n_{I1}	n_{I2}	$\ldots$	n_{Ij}	$\ldots$	n_{IJ}	$n_{I.}$
	$n_{.1}$	$n_{.2}$	$\ldots$	$n_{.j}$	$\ldots$	$n_{.J}$	$n_{..} = N$

FIGURE 3-6-2. Sample information for problem 3-6-5

The quantity n_{ij} is the number of persons in category i who most often buy soap j. The total number of persons in category i is given by $n_{i.} = \sum_{j=1}^{J} n_{ij}$ and the total number who buy soap j the most is given by $n_{.j} = \sum_{i=1}^{I} n_{ij}$. (These quantities appear in the margin in the table.) Because of this tabular presentation, this type of problem is called a *contingency table problem*.

Using the likelihood ratio method it is possible to determine that

$$\lambda = \frac{\prod_{i=1}^{I} n_{i.}^{n_{i.}} \prod_{j=1}^{J} n_{.j}^{n_{.j}}}{n_{..}^{n_{..}} \prod_{i=1}^{I} \prod_{j=1}^{J} n_{ij}^{n_{ij}}}$$

There are two difficulties in using the likelihood ratio statistic λ to test the hypothesis of (3-6-24): First, λ is difficult to compute; second, and more serious, the probability distribution of λ cannot be obtained under the null hypothesis since it depends upon q_i and r_j which are unknown. These difficulties can be lessened somewhat by considering the quantity $L = -2 \log \lambda$. L is easier to compute since it involves sums rather than products, but it still involves computing logarithms. An approximation to the probability distribution of L can also be obtained for very large N which does not depend upon q_i and r_j.

To better resolve these difficulties with the likelihood ratio statistic,

$$w = \sum_{i=1}^{I} \sum_{j=1}^{J} \frac{(n_{ij} - (m_{i.}n_{.j}/n_{..}))^2}{n_{i.}n_{.j}/n_{..}} \qquad (3\text{-}6\text{-}25)$$

has been proposed, instead, as the statistic upon which the test should be based. Reasonable estimates for the unknown quantities p_{ij}, q_i and r_j are the estimators $\hat{p}_{ij} = n_{ij}/n_{..}$, $\hat{q}_i = n_{i.}/n_{..}$ and $\hat{r}_j = n_{.j}/n_{..}$. If the null hypotheses is true, then it should be approximately true that $\hat{p}_{ij} = \hat{q}_i \hat{r}_j$. Therefore $(\hat{p}_{ij} - \hat{q}_i \hat{r}_j)^2$ should be small for every value of i and j, that quantity being the numerator of (3-6-25) apart from a factor of $n_{..}^2$. The denominator of (3-6-25) is needed to obtain the approximate distribution of w when the null hypothesis is true and the values of q_i and r_j are unknown. The statistic w is easily computed since it involves only sums and products. It is possible to show that when the null hypothesis is true, it has a χ^2 distribution with $(I - 1)(J - 1)$ degrees of freedom. This approximation has been found to be good for much smaller values of N than is the approximation to the distribution of the statistic L. Therefore the statistic w resolves the two difficulties which were encountered in trying to use the likelihood ratio statistic. The critical region is of the form that one rejects the null hypothesis if $w > k$ where k is selected from tables of the χ^2 distribution, so that the region has a size α.

Exercises

3-1. For each of the following, state the probability density functions belonging to the null and the alternative hypotheses:

(a) There are two groups of high school students who have different abilities in mathematics and are to be assigned to different courses. On a standardized test, one group has scores which are normally distributed with a mean of 90% and a standard deviation of 1%, whereas the other group has scores which are normally distributed with a mean of 85% and a standard deviation of 1%. One group is to be assigned when it is realized that their records have been misplaced, so the advisor does not know which group he is advising. To find out, he retests two students and, based on the scores, he will make his decision.

(b) A student who is not prepared for a true–false examination is offered a "lucky" coin by his friend. His friend says it is lucky because it has a higher probability of heads than tails. The student in order to verify the statement tosses the coin twice and, based on the outcome, makes his decision.

3-2. Which of the hypotheses stated in Exercise 3-1 are simple and which are composite?

3-3. Graph the following critical regions:

(a) $R_1 = \{(x_1, x_2) \,|\, |x_1 + x_2| \le 1\}$
(b) $R_2 = \{(x_1, x_2) \,|\, x_2 \ge x_1^2 - 1\}$
(c) $R_3 = \{(x_1, x_2) \,|\, x_1^2 + 2x_2^2 \le 2\}$
(d) $R_4 = \{(x_1, x_2) \,|\, x_1^2 + x_2^2 \ge 4\}$

3-4. For each of the critical regions in Exercise 3-3, determine whether or not each of the following points falls in the region:

(a) $(1, 1)$ (b) $(0, 0)$
(c) $(\frac{1}{2}, 1)$ (d) $(1, \frac{1}{2})$
(e) $(-1, \frac{1}{2})$ (f) $(1, -1)$

3-5. In Problem 3-2-1 assume that a sample of size 3 is drawn. Compute the size of the regions

$$R_1 = \{(1, 0, 1) \quad (1, 1, 0) \quad (1, 0, 1)\}$$
$$R_2 = \{(1, 0, 0) \quad (0, 0, 0) \quad (1, 1, 1)\}$$
$$R_3 = \{(1, 0, 0) \quad (0, 1, 0) \quad (0, 0, 1)\}$$

3-6. For the regions of Exercise 3-5 which have the same size, compute the power against all alternatives. Are any regions inadmissible?

3-7. For the densities given in Exercise 1-6, use the Neyman-Pearson Lemma to construct a most powerful test for the problem with $H_0: f(x, \theta_0)$ and $H_1: f(x, \theta_1)$ where $\theta_1 > \theta_0$. Where $\theta_1 < \theta_0$.

3-8. For the probability density functions in Exercise 1-4 find the likelihood ratio test to test the simple null hypothesis $\theta = \theta_0$ against the composite alternative hypothesis $\theta \in \Omega, \theta \neq \theta_0$.

3-9. For the probability density functions of Exercise 1-6, parts (a) and (c), find the likelihood ratio test to test the simple null hypothesis $\theta = \theta_0$ against the composite alternative hypothesis $\theta \in \Omega, \theta \neq \theta_0$.

3-10. Use the critical region obtained in Exercise 3-8 to obtain a confidence interval estimate for the unknown parameter of the probability density functions of Exercise 1-4.

3-11. Use the critical region obtained in Exercise 3-9 to obtain a confidence interval estimate for the unknown parameter of the probability density functions of Exercise 1-6, parts (a) and (c).

3-12. For Problem 3-7-1 find the confidence coefficient for the confidence interval estimate of the parameter a when:

(a) $L(X_1, X_2) = (X_1 + X_2)/2 - 2 \qquad U(X_1, X_2) = (X_1 + X_2)/2$
(b) $L(X_1, X_2) = (X_1 + X_2)/2 - 1$

$$U(X_1, X_2) = (X_1 + X_2)/2 + 1$$

3-13. If, in Problem 3-7-1, we take a sample of size 3, with replacement, and use $L(X_1, X_2, X_3) = (X_1 + X_2 + X_3)/3 - 1$ and $U(X_1, X_2, X_3) = (X_1 + X_2 + X_3)/3 + 2$ in forming the confidence interval estimate of the parameter a, then what is the confidence coefficient?

3-14. In Problem 3-6-1, assume the 6 transistors were tested and their lifespans were $x_1 = 1050$, $x_2 = 1121$, $x_3 = 982$, $x_4 = 990$, $x_5 = 1062$, $x_6 = 1115$. Test the null hypothesis that $\mu_0 = 1000$. using a critical region of size $\alpha = .05$.

3-15. Consider the observations of Exercise 3-14 and use them to test the null hypothesis that $\sigma^2 = 5$ in Problem 3-6-2, using a critical region of size $\alpha = .10$.

3-16. In Problem 3-6-3, assume that the test results yielded the following data: $x_1 = 267$, $x_2 = 412$, $x_3 = 159$, $x_4 = 274$, $x_5 = 193$, $y_1 = 285$, $y_2 = 321$, $y_3 = 225$, $y_4 = 182$. Test the null hypothesis that $\mu_x = \mu_y$ using a critical region of size $\alpha = .01$.

3-17. Consider the observations of Exercise 3-16. Use them to test the null hypothesis that $\sigma_x^2 = \sigma_y^2$ in Problem 3-6-4, using a critical region of size $\alpha = .05$.

3–18. From past experience a certain receiving station could process 50 orders per day. A new procedure was introduced, and for the next two weeks the number of orders received per day were 38, 42, 48, 43, 58, 41, 52, 68, 50, and 53. If we assume that the number of orders is a normal random variable can we conclude that the new procedure has significantly changed the number of orders which can be processed? Choose $\alpha = .01$.

3–19. If in Exercise 3–18 from past experience it was known that the variance was equal to 4, can we conclude that the new procedure has changed the variance? Choose $\alpha = .05$.

3–20. A company is planning to buy a new computer and they have narrowed the choice to only two. The company's data processing manager obtains data from companies having similar types of jobs to perform concerning the running time of these jobs:

Machine A

Job #	Running Time
1	25
2	30
3	48
4	50
5	27

Machine B

Job #	Running Time
1	18
2	29
3	40
4	52
5	31
6	38
7	25

Can the data processing manager conclude that the machines have different running times with $\alpha = .05$? What assumptions must he make before making these conclusions?

3–21. In Problem 3–6–5 assume there are four income groups and three types of soap, and the results of our sample of 300 people are:

	B_1	B_2	B_3	
A_1	30	20	25	75
A_2	40	30	50	120
A_3	20	15	15	50
A_4	20	20	15	55
	110	85	105	300

Determine if there is any relationship between income and the type of soap used. Use $\alpha = .05$.

3-22. A college English instructor is trying to determine if a person's grade in the basic English composition course is independent of sex. He has compiled information about the grades given in this course for the last three years, as follows:

Grade	Male	Female
A	48	62
B	120	122
C	223	236
D	85	62
F	24	18

At the .01 level of significance, can the instructor conclude that a person's sex and grade are independent?

chapter four

Decision Making

4-1. INTRODUCTION

In chapter two, the problem under consideration was that of using the information contained in a sample to select a value for an unknown paramater from a collection of possible values for that parameter. Although this was the explicit problem, it was always implied that there would be some further use made of the estimated value. Once he has determined the estimate of λ, the distributor of appliances (Problem 1-1-1) will use that particular Poisson distribution to predict demand, and then make some decision as to the number of gas ranges to stock. In Problem 1-1-3, when the proportion of *Life* subscribers who also subscribed to *Time* is estimated, some decision as to advertising policies will be made. Note that the problem of estimation is, in fact, a type of decision problem since we are making a decision in order to select one value from the many possible values of the parameter. The type of decision problem discussed in this chapter will differ in that costs and other economic considerations will be specified in the model. With this methodology, then, we will be required to supply more information in the development of the basic model. If this information is not available, then the methods of chapter two can still be used with the final decision (usually some type of action) being implicit, rather than explicit, in the model.

The last chapter was devoted to a special type of problem where only two decisions were available—to favor the null hypothesis or the alternative hypothesis. Again, once that was decided, there was still another action to take, based on certain economic considerations which were not explicitly stated in the model. Since the problems of Chapters 2 and 3 are special types, certainly any general theory of decision making should include them as special cases. This was accomplished by Abraham Wald who developed the general approach to statistical decision making by explicitly including cost and other economic considerations into the mathematical model being considered. The special cases, then, are included into the general theory by the definition of an artificial cost structure. We will not consider the general statistical decision formulation and, therefore, we will only be able to indicate how estimation and hypothesis testing problem are special cases of this general approach. Our objective will be to introduce and to illustrate some of the additional concepts which are necessary in making decisions by using this general theory.

Recall that the general definition of a statistical problem requires that we have a probabilistic model with certain unspecified elements. In addition, we require sample information from which we will make some inference. The statistical decision making problem is no different, but we will approach it in stages.

4–2. DECISION MAKING—NO PRIOR PROBABILITIES—NO SAMPLING

To illustrate the method of decision making of this section consider the following example.

Problem 4-2-1. A teenage boy, at Christmas time, forms a Christmas tree business. He drives to a tree farm where he is able to buy as many trees as he needs at $1.00 each. Since his truck will only hold 5 trees he may buy no more. He will be able to sell the trees for $3 each if he is able to sell them at all. Otherwise he will get nothing for the trees. Assume that the truck belongs to his father and there are no transportation costs. The demand for the trees will be assumed as a random variable. The boy must decide how many Christmas trees to buy.

First, note that this model explicitly includes cost and selling price information which enables us to compute profits. The profits are usually presented in a table called a reward or *payoff table*. The possible decisions which the boy can make are given in the upper margin and the possible number of trees demanded (events) are given in the left margin. The entries in the body of the table are the profit obtained for a particular event-decision combination. Thus, if one tree is bought and if there is a demand for one tree, the entry in the table for the column corresponding to that decision is \$3 − \$1 = \$2. Continuing in this manner, we obtain Figure 4-2-1.

Decisions

Quantity demanded		Buy 0 d_0	Buy 1 d_1	Buy 2 d_2	Buy 3 d_3	Buy 4 d_4	Buy 5 d_5
0	e_0	\$0	−\$1	−\$2	−\$3	−\$4	−\$5
1	e_1	\$0	\$2	\$1	\$0	−\$1	−\$2
2	e_2	\$0	\$2	\$4	\$3	\$2	\$1
3	e_3	\$0	\$2	\$4	\$6	\$5	\$4
4	e_4	\$0	\$2	\$4	\$6	\$8	\$7
5 or more	e_5	\$0	\$2	\$4	\$6	\$8	\$10

FIGURE 4-2-1. Payoff table for problem 4-2-1

If we indicate the decision to buy j trees by $d_j (j = 0, 1, 2, 3, 4, 5)$ and the event that there is a demand for i trees by $e_i (i = 0, 1, 2, 3, 4, 5)$, then the payoff function can be denoted by $r(e_i, d_j)$. We may define the entries in the table as follows:

$$r(e_i, d_j) = \begin{array}{ll} \$ (3i - j) & j \leq i \\ \$ 2j & i > j \end{array} \qquad (4\text{-}2\text{-}1)$$

In general we are presented with a situation in which we have a finite or an infinite number of possible decisions and a finite or an infinite number of possible events. In order to apply the methods of statistical decision theory, enough information must be specified in the model to define the payoff function for each event-decision combination. This limits application of the theory. We will only consider the case in which there are a finite number of possible decisions and a finite number of possible events.

The difficulty involved in selecting a decision (d_j) from the payoff table information is that we do not know which event (e_i) will occur. Once the table has been computed, one method of making a decision may be reasoned: For each decision (d_j), determine the smallest possible payoff, min $r(e_i, d_j)$, denoted by $s(d_j)$. If decision d_j is made, the function $s(d_j)$ indicates the worst possible payoff. The criterion for selecting d_j, which will be called the maximin payoff criterion, selects the d_j which will maximize $s(d_j)$—that is, the decision which gives the best of the worst possible payoffs. For the payoff table (Figure 4-2-1) we obtain $s(d_0) = \$0$, $s(d_1) = -\$1$, $s(d_2) = -\$2$, $s(d_3) = -\$3$ $s(d_4) = -\$4$, and $s(d_5) = -\$5$ which, upon applying the maximin payoff criterion, indicates d_0 is the best decision. This criterion is indeed conservative since it assures the boy that he won't lose anything. But it also assures him that he won't gain anything. In general, then, this method will protect against making decisions which could lead to losses at the expense of giving up any opportunity to make large profits (see Figure 4-2-2). Applying the maximin payoff criteria, we obtain that $s(d_0) = \$0$, $s(d_1) = -\$.01$, and $s(d_2) = -\$.01$ from which we conclude that the best decision is d_0. And we give up the possibility of making \$10,000, in order to avoid the possibility of losing \$.01, when e_0 occurs.

Decisions

Events	d_0	d_1	d_2
e_0	\$0.00	$-\$.01$	$-\$.01$
e_1	\$0.00	\$10,000.	\$10,000.
e_2	\$0.00	\$10,000.	\$10,000.

FIGURE 4-2-2. Payoff table for three-decision problem I

To try to resolve this type of situation, let us consider the concept of an *opportunity loss function*, denoted by $q(e_i, d_j)$, which is defined by the relation

$$q(e_i, d_j) = \max_{j'} r(e_i, d_{j'}) - r(e_i, d_j) \qquad (4\text{-}2\text{-}2)$$

Operationally, to form an opportunity loss table corresponding to $q(e_i, d_j)$, we proceed row by row. Find the maximum payoff for a given row, and then subtract from this maximum payoff each element in that row which gives some measure of how the payoffs from various decisions will differ from the best decision for that event. The opportunity loss tables corresponding to the payoff tables (Figures 4-2-1 and 4-2-2) are given in Figures 4-2-3 and 4-2-4. Note from the definition of the function $q(e_i, d_j)$ which we present in tabular form in the opportunity loss table that all entries must be greater than or equal to zero.

To select a decision using the the opportunity loss table we use the same reasoning as was used when the information available was the payoff table. We first compute the function $t(d_j) = \max_{i} q(e_i, d_j)$ which gives for

Decisions

Events	d_0	d_1	d_2	d_3	d_4	d_5
e_0	$ 0	$1	$2	$3	$4	$5
e_1	2	0	1	2	3	4
e_2	4	2	0	1	2	3
e_3	6	4	2	0	1	2
e_4	8	6	4	2	0	1
e_5	10	8	6	4	2	0

FIGURE 4-2-3. Opportunity loss table for problem 4-2-1

Decisions

Events	d_0	d_1	d_2
e_0	$.00	$.01	$.01
e_1	10,000	.00	.00
e_2	10,000	.00	.00

FIGURE 4-2-4. Opportunity loss table for three-decision problem I

each decision d_j the largest possible opportunity loss. We then select the decision d_j which gives the smallest value of the function $t(d_j)$. For each decision we have first taken the worst possible situation in terms of opportunity loss given by $t(d_j)$ and then we have selected the decision for which we obtain the best of these worst possible situations. We will call this criterion the *minimax opportunity loss criterion*.

For Figure 4-2-3 we obtain that $t(d_0) = \$10$, $t(d_1) = \$8$, $t(d_2) = \$6$, $t(d_3) = \$4$, $t(d_4) = \$4$, and $t(d_5) = \$5$. Since the smallest value of $t(d_j)$ is $t(d_3) = t(d_4) = \$4$, we can make decision d_3 or d_4. We are led to a different decision from that obtained using the maximin payoff criterion. This is not surprising since the two criteria lead to different decisions, protecting against different consequences; the maximin payoff criterion protects against a large absolute loss, whereas the minimax opportunity loss protects against a large loss relative to the best possible action for a given event as measured by opportunity loss. For Figure 4-2-4 we obtain that the function $t(d_j)$ is given by $t(d_0) = \$10,000$, $t(d_1) = \$.01$, and $t(d_2) = \$.01$ from which it follows that we should make decision d_1 or d_2, whereas the maximin payoff criteria led to the selection of decision d_0. In this case we can see more clearly that the relative loss, measured by the opportunity loss suffered by making decision d_0, is much greater than if we make decision d_1 or d_2. Determining which criteria to use depends upon one's attitude toward suffering various types of losses.

Now, let us consider an example which illustrates that the maximin payoff criteria and the minimax opportunity loss criteria can lead to the *same* decision.

Decisions

Events	d_0	d_1	d_2
e_0	.00	$-$$.01	$10,000
e_1	.00	10,000	$-$ .01
e_2	.00	10,000	10,000

FIGURE 4-2-5. Payoff table for three-decision problem II

Decisions

Events	d_0	d_1	d_2
e_0	$10,000	$10,000.01	$.00
e_1	10,000	.00	10,000.01
e_2	10,000	.00	.00

FIGURE 4-2-6. Opportunity loss table for three-decision problem II

From Figure 4-2-5 we obtain that $s(d_0) = \$0$, $s(d_1) = -\$.01$, and $s(d_2) = -\$.01$; from Figure 4-2-6 we obtain that $t(d_0) = \$10,000$, $t(d_1) = \$10,000.01$, and $t(d_2) = \$10,000.01$. It follows that both the maximin payoff criterion and the minimax opportunity loss criterion lead to selecting decision d_0. If we change the payoff table by changing the row corresponding to the event e_2 as follows: $r(e_2, d_0) = \$0$, $r(e_2, d_1) = \$0$, and $r(e_2, d_2) = \$0$, the corresponding change in the opportunity loss table would be $q(e_2, d_0) = \$0$, $q(e_2, d_1) = \$0$, and $q(e_2, d_2) = \$0$. The functions $s(d_j)$ and $t(d_j)$ are unchanged, however, so the decision selected will be the same. Another disadvantage of these two criteria is that they are influenced only by the extremes of the payoff and opportunity loss table rather than by the entire table. Also, the payoff table and corresponding opportunity loss table are constructed such that all possible events are included. But we have not taken into account the fact that some events may not occur in practice although they are theoretical possibilities. The teenage boy *may*, in fact, rely upon selling at least one Christmas tree—to his father. Where no attention is paid to the frequency with which the various events occur, the criteria used may lead to decisions protecting events that are not likely to occur. Methods of avoiding these difficulties are presented next.

4–3. DECISION MAKING—PRIOR PROBABILITIES—NO SAMPLING

In this section we will assume that, in addition to the payoff function $r(e_i, d_j)$ $(i = 0, 1, \ldots, I; j = 0, 1, \ldots, J)$, we are also given the probabilities $p_i(i - 0, 1, \ldots, I)$ with which the event e_i occurs. These are called *prior probabilities* since they are known prior to the drawing of a sample. If we consider Problem 4-2-1, e_i is the event that i Christmas trees are demanded for that particular Christmas season. Two questions, concerning the probabilities $p_i(i = 0, 1, \ldots, I)$, now arise. First, how can these probabilities be determined? And second, how can these probabilities be interpreted?

The usual interpretation of a probability, p_i, is that it is approximately equal to the relative frequency with which an event, e_i, occurs in repeated observations of the same experiment. Thus, if we have two possible events, e_0(heads) and e_1(tails), which may occur as the result of a coin toss, probabilities p_0 and p_1 would be interpreted as the relative frequencies with which heads and tails occur in a large number of tosses (of the same coin, under the same conditions). This interpretation also leads to a method of determining the probabilities p_i through experimentation or, as we prefer to call it, through sampling.

For Problem 4-2-1, it is necessary to determine the prior probabilities for the Christmas season without sampling. It is quite conceivable, however, that the previous Christmas season was similar to this season. By asking 30 classmates about how many trees they were able to sell last year, the boy may be able to determine a relative frequency distribution for the events $e_i(i = 0, 1, 2, 3, 4, 5)$, which is given in Figure 4-3-1.

Event	e_0	e_1	e_2	e_3	e_4	e_5
Relative frequency	.1	.1	.2	.1	.2	.3

FIGURE 4-3-1. Relative frequency data for problem 4-2-1

From this information he might be willing to equate the relation frequency of the event e_i, in the previous year, to the prior probability of the event e_i, and it would be possible to obtain the values p_i. The interpretation of the p_i values, in this case, might be that if the whole class of 30 boys sold Christmas trees this year, the relative frequency of the events e_i might be approximately equal to p_i. This information might be of interest to a corporation hiring the whole group to sell trees, but an individual is concerned with his own chances of selling trees. Therefore, we would like to give an interpretation to the probabilities p_i which may differ from person to person. This is a *subjective* or *personal probability*. The reason for needing this type of interpretation may be seen from an examination of the probability p_0 of the event e_0. If we examine the relative frequencies in Figure 4-3-1 and equate these to the prior probabilities, we obtain $p_0 = .1$. In this particular case, if the boy knows that his father will buy one tree, he would select his personal probability $p_0 = 0$ since the event e_0 is impossible. Inability to determine these personal prior probabilities may make the application of this procedure in practical problems difficult.

One method of determining these probabilities is based on the *standard gamble* interpretation. Suppose that we have a wheel, similar to a roulette wheel, with numbers 1 through 100. When the wheel is spun, the ball with equal probability—that is, with probability .01—will land in any numbered hole. We interpret this probability in terms of relative frequency over a large number of trials. For example, we will say that e_1 has subjective probability $p_1 = .2$, if we are given the choice of (a) receiving $1 when e_1 occurs, or (b) receiving $1 when any number between 1 and 20, inclusive, comes up in a turn of the wheel, but we are indifferent between the two choices. To obtain the set of numbers given in choice (b) that makes us indifferent is a complex procedure. First, we might consider, in (b), the numbers 1 through 10 which would make us prefer choice (a). We then know that we have included too few numbers. So, next, we might consider the numbers 1 through 30 which would make us prefer choice (b). Now we have included too many numbers, and we know that the appropriate set consists of numbers somewhere between 10 and 30. By continually reducing the set of numbers, we eventually find that the set of numbers 1 through 20 would make us indifferent. The subjection probability p_i of the event e_i is then said to be equal to the probability that a number in the given set appears; thus, in our example we take $p_i = .2$ since the probability of obtaining a number between 1 and 20 is .2. Many times, of course, the subjective probability of e_i is the same as the relative frequency of e_i. In similar though not identical situations, this is the only information which may be available for deciding whether or not we should be indifferent betweeen the choices available. It is possible, however, to incorporate all of this information in the determination of whether or not we are indifferent between the choices available. Assume that, based on this type of reasoning, it is possible to obtain prior subjective probabilities, as in Figure 4-3-2.

Once the subjective prior probabilities have been determined, we compute the function $u(d_j) = \sum_{i=0}^{I} r(e_i, d_j)p_i$ which is the expected payoff for each decision. The decision criterion is to select the decision (d_j) which maximizes the expected payoff function. We might also consider and compute the expected opportunity loss function, $v(d_j) = \sum_{i=1}^{I} q(e_i, d_j)p_i$. The decision criterion in that case would be to select the decision (d_j) which minimizes the expected opportunity loss function. It can easily be shown that either criterion will lead to the same decision d_j. For the payoff function in Figure 4-2-1, we have that $u(d_0) = \$0$, $u(d_1) = \$2$, $u(d_2) = \$3.40$, $u(d_3) = \$4.20$, $u(d_4) = \$4.70$, and $u(d_5) = \$4.60$, whereas $v(d_0) = \$6.40$, $v(d_1) = \$4.40$, $v(d_2) = \$3$, $v(d_3) = \$2.20$, $v(d_4) = \$1.70$, and $v(d_5) = \$1.80$. So for both criteria, the appropriate decision is d_4, since the minimum of $v(d_j)$ and the maximum of $u(d_j)$ both occur at d_4.

Events	e_0	e_1	e_2	e_3	e_4	e_5
Prior probabilities	0	.2	.2	.1	.2	.3

**FIGURE 4-3-2. Prior probability distribution
for problem 4-2-1**

Let us now consider the familiar decision problem of whether or not to buy fire insurance on a home for the next year. The basic elements of the problem—the payoff function and the prior probabilities—are presented by Figure 4-3-3. The decision to buy insurance will guarantee a yearly loss of $100, the cost of the premium. But a loss of $25,000 will occur if the house is destroyed by fire. We have simplified the problem by considering only two events: e_0, the house is completely destroyed by fire; or e_1, there is no fire. A more realistic model might include more events, admitting the possibility of partial destruction of the house, and more decisions, involving various insurance policies. From the information in the figure we find that $u(d_0) = -\$100$ and $u(d_1) = -25$. By using the criterion of maximizing the expected payoff function we arrive at a decision not to buy any insurance. But this is contrary to the behavior of most

Decisions

Prior probabilities	Events	Buy insurance d_0	Do not buy insurance d_1
.001	fire (e_0)	−$100	−$25,000
.999	no fire (e_1)	−$100	$0

**FIGURE 4-3-3. Payoff table for insurance
problem**

people and should lead us to question whether this criterion for decision making is a useful one.

The difficulty involved here is not that the *expected* payoff function is the wrong function to maximize, but that we have selected the wrong payoff function. In this problem, the loss of one's home (which is usually the most expensive and most valued single material possession that a person owns) could not be measured by the monetary value of the loss. This has led researchers in decision making to introduce units, other than money, for defining the payoff function, which we call *utilities*. It can then be shown by an axiomatic development that maximizing the expected payoff function when payoffs are defined in utility units is an appropriate method of decision making. If there are not extreme monetary payoffs— that is, *extremely* large profits of *extremely* large losses—then the definitions of the payoff function, in terms of utility units or monetary units, are equivalent. Since there are practical difficulties in determining the payoff function in terms of utility units, we will not consider this problem. It is merely emphasized that the decision criterion of maximizing the expected monetary payoff function is only applicable when there are no extreme payoffs.

4–4. DECISION MAKING—NO PRIOR PROBABILITIES—SAMPLING

The introduction of sample data gives additional information concerning which event e_i prevails. Here, a new concept must be added to the method outlined in the last two sections; it is that of a *decision rule*, sometimes called a *decision function*. We encountered this concept in Chapter 3, only under different terminology. Looking at Problem 3-2-1 from the new viewpoint, we consider $e_i(i\ 0, 1, 2, 3, 4)$ to be the event that there are i red balls in the urn. The simple null hypothesis that there are 2 red and 2 black balls in the urn consists of the single event e_2; and the alternative hypothesis consists of the remaining events, $e_i(i = 0, 1, 3, 4)$. The decisions which we may make are that the null hypothesis is true (d_0) or the alternative hypothesis is true (d_1). The payoff function is given in Figure 4-4-1. This fictitious payoff function awards one unit for a correct decision and nothing for a wrong decision. An application of the maximin payoff criteria will not lead to any decision since $s(d_0) = s(d_1) = 0$.

We would proceed by taking a sample of arbitrary size N and selecting a critical region R. If the sample point $(x_1, x_2, \ldots, x_N)$ belongsto R, we would accept the alternative hypothesis; if the sample point $(x_1, x_2, \ldots, x_N)$ does not belong to R, we would accept the null hypothesis.

Decisions

Events	d_0	d_1
e_0	0	1
e_1	0	1
e_2	1	0
e_3	0	1
e_4	0	1

FIGURE 4-4-1. Payoff table for problem 3-2-1

Another way of presenting this same argument is to state that the N-dimensional Euclidian space is divided into two parts, R and $\bar{R}$, where R is the critical region (now called the *rejection region*) and $\bar{R}$ consists of all points in the N-dimensional Euclidian space not belonging to R (now called the *acceptance region*). If a sample point falls in $\bar{R}$, we make decision d_0, whereas if a point falls in R we make the decision d_1. This method of selecting a decision on the basis of a sample is called a *decision rule*. Thus, for every test of hypothesis, we can define a corresponding decision rule.

Decisions

Events	d_0	d_1
e_0	1	0
e_1	1	0
e_2	0	1
e_3	1	0
e_4	1	0

FIGURE 4-4-2. Opportunity loss table for problem 3-2-1

In order to evaluate the performance of a decision rule, it will be more convenient to use the opportunity loss function, rather than the payoff function, but similar reasoning may be used in the latter case. The opportunity loss table corresponding to the payoff table (Figure 4-4-1) is shown in Figure 4-4-2.

Considering the case of a sample of size $N = 2$, where we use the notation of Problem 3-2-1, a decision rule may be defined:

> *Decision rule $\delta^{(1)}$*
> Decide d_0 if (X_1, X_2) belongs to $\bar{R}_1 = \{(0, 1), (1, 0)\}$
> Decide d_1 if (X_1, X_2) belongs to $R_1 = \{(1, 0), (0, 1)\}$ (4-4-1)

According to our previous definition, the region $\bar{\mathbf{R}}_1$ should consist of all points (X_1, X_2) not belonging to R_1—that is, all points except $(1, 0)$ and $(0, 1)$. If $\bar{\mathbf{R}}_1$ is defined either in this way or as in (4-4-1), we will decide d_1 only when either $(0, 1)$ or $(1, 0)$ occurs. Note that the decision rule $\delta^{(1)}$ makes decisions d_0 and d_1 with certain probabilities, and that these probabilities depend upon which event e_i prevails; that is,

$$P\{\delta^{(1)} = d_0 \,|\, e_i\} = P\{(X_1, X_2) \text{ belongs to } \bar{\mathbf{R}}_1 \,|\, e_i\}$$

and

$$P\{\delta^{(1)} = d_1 \,|\, e_i\} = P\{(X_1, X_2) \text{ belongs to } R_1 \,|\, e_i\} \qquad (4\text{-}4\text{-}2)$$

The function that we shall use in evaluating the performance of the decision rule is defined by:

$$w(e_i, \delta^{(1)}) = \sum_{j=0}^{1} q(e_i, d_j) P\{\delta^{(1)} = d_j \,|\, e_i\} \qquad (4\text{-}4\text{-}3)$$

which is interpreted as the expected opportunity loss under the condition that e_i prevails; $\delta^{(1)}$ is the decision rule. From (4-4-3) we obtain for $i = 0$, 1, 3, 4, that:

$$
\begin{aligned}
w(e_i, \delta^{(1)}) &= 1 \cdot P\{\delta^{(1)} = d_0 \,|\, e_i\} + 0 \cdot P\{\delta^{(1)} = d_1 \,|\, e_i\} \\
&= P\{\delta^{(1)} = d_0 \,|\, e_i\} \\
&= P\{(X_1, X_2) \text{ belongs to } \bar{\mathbf{R}}_1 \,|\, e_i\} \\
&= 1 - P\{(X_1, X_2) \text{ belongs to } R_1 \,|\, e_i\} \qquad (4\text{-}4\text{-}4)
\end{aligned}
$$

whereas for $i = 2$:

$$
\begin{aligned}
w(e_2, \delta^{(1)}) &= 0 \cdot P\{\delta^{(1)} = d_0 \,|\, e_2\} + 1 \cdot P\{\delta^{(1)} = d_1 \,|\, e_2\} \\
&= P\{\delta^{(1)} = d_1 \,|\, e_2\} \\
&= P\{(X_1, X_2) \text{ belongs to } R_1 \,|\, e_2\} \qquad (4\text{-}4\text{-}5)
\end{aligned}
$$

In this type of two-decision problem, with the given opportunity loss function, the conditional expected opportunity loss $w(e_2, \delta^{(1)})$ gives the size of the critical region R_1, and the values of $w(e_i, \delta^{(1)})\, i = 0, 1, 3, 4$ give 1 minus the power of region R_1.

In decision making problems, however, we use the information contained in the power functions or, equivalently, in $w(e_i, \delta^{(1)})$ in a different way than in hypothesis testing to choose between various decision rules. Consider the regions $R_2 = \{(1, 1), (0, 0)\}$ and $R_3 = \{(0, 0), (0, 1)\}$, which we considered in Problem 3-2-1. We can define corresponding decision rules $\delta^{(2)}$ and $\delta^{(3)}$, in a manner similar to the method used to define $\delta^{(1)}$ from R_1, and compute the corresponding conditional expected opportunity loss functions $w(e_i, \delta^{(2)})$ and $w(e_i, \delta^{(3)})$, presented in Figure 4-4-3. If we consider the entries in this table of expected opportunity losses as an opportunity loss table, then we can use the reasoning of Section 4-2

Decisions

Events	$\delta^{(1)}$	$\delta^{(2)}$	$\delta^{(3)}$
e_0	1	0	1
e_1	10/16	6/16	12/16
e_2	1/2	1/2	1/2
e_3	10/16	6/16	4/16
e_4	1	0	0

FIGURE 4-4-3. Conditional expected opportunity loss function for problem 3-2-1

to choose the best decision rule. By applying the minimax opportunity loss criteria, we obtain the function $t(\delta^{(J)}) = \max w(e_i, \delta^{(J)})$ to be $t(\delta^{(1)}) = 1$, $t(\delta^{(2)}) = 1/2$, and $t(\delta^{(3)}) = 1$, from which we choose the best decision rule to be $\delta^{(2)}$. The concept of an admissible and inadmissible decision rule may be defined in a manner analogous to the corresponding concepts for critical regions; that is, a decision rule is inadmissible if there is another decision rule which gives at least as small an opportunity loss for each possible event e_i. Thus, $\delta^{(1)}$ is an inadmissible decision rule. (A decision rule which is not inadmissible is, of course, admissible.)

Consider, next, a slight modification of Problem 4-2-1:

Problem 4-4-1. Suppose that by use of the minimax opportunity loss criterion the boy has decided to buy 3 Christmas trees. Upon arrival at the farm, he is told that they will not sell fewer than 5 trees to any individual. Now in order to make his decision, he tries to use some sampling by mentally going through his possible customers. He determines that there are 10 possibilities, and decides to call, at random, two of these people and ask them if they would be interested in buying Christmas trees. Based on the number of affirmative replies, the boy will decide whether to buy 5 trees or no trees.

There are now two possible decisions for the problem: buy no trees (d_0), or buy five trees (d_1). The payoff function and opportunity loss function for this problem are given in Figures 4-4-4 and 4-4-5. In this problem, and in all problems in which we sample, it is necessary to define the events such that they are single outcomes rather than a collection of outcomes. In Problem 4-2-1, by event e_5 we meant that the demand was 5 or 6 or 7, etc., which is a collection of outcomes. In this problem, we mean by e_5 the event that exactly 5 trees are demanded, and the largest i we consider is $i = 10$ since there are only 10 possible customers.

Decisions

Events	d_0	d_1
e_0	$0	−$5
e_1	$0	−$2
e_2	$0	+$1
e_3	$0	+$4
e_4	$0	+$7
e_5	$0	+$10
e_6	$0	+$10
e_7	$0	+$10
e_8	$0	+$10
e_9	$0	+$10
e_{10}	$0	+$10

FIGURE 4-4-4. Payoff table for problem 4-4-1

Decisions

Events	d_0	d_1
e_0	$0	$5
e_1	$0	$2
e_2	$1	$0
e_3	$4	$0
e_4	$7	$0
e_5	$10	$0
e_6	$10	$0
e_7	$10	$0
e_8	$10	$0
e_9	$10	$0
e_{10}	$10	$0

FIGURE 4-4-5. Opportunity loss table for problem 4-4-1

We now consider the three decision rules $\delta^{(k)}$.

> If there are k or fewer affirmative answers
>   select decision d_0
> If there are more than k affirmative answers
>   select decision d_1 (4-4-6)

where $k = 0, 1, 2$. To select the best decision rule, we must determine the expected opportunity loss function $w(e_i, \delta^{(k)})$ ($i = 0, 1, \ldots, 10$; $k = 0$,

1, 2). When the event e_i prevails, we will mean that of the 10 potential customers i would answer affirmatively, when called, as well as that i would buy Christmas trees. By the same reasoning as we previously used, we obtain:

$$w(e_i, \delta^{(k)}) = \sum_{j=0}^{1} q(e_i, d_j) P\{\delta^{(k)} = d_j \mid e_i\} \qquad (4\text{-}4\text{-}7)$$

The only new quantity to compute is $P\{\delta^{(k)} = d_j \mid e_i\}$. To do this, we define a random variable, X_2, as the number of affirmative answers in two calls, where X_2 is a hypergeometric random variable. From (4-4-6), we have that:

$$P\{\delta^{(k)} = d_0 \mid e_i\} = P\{X_2 \le k \mid e_i\}$$
$$P\{\delta^{(k)} = d_1 \mid e_i\} = P\{X_2 > k \mid e_i\} \qquad (4\text{-}4\text{-}8)$$

To compute the probabilities on the right of (4-4-8), we need an expression for $P\{X_2 = y \mid e_i\}$, denoted by $\pi(e_i, y)$.

$$\pi(0, 0) = 1 \qquad \pi(0, 1) = 0 \qquad \pi(0, 2) = 0$$

$$\pi(1, 0) = \frac{\binom{9}{2}}{\binom{10}{2}} \qquad \pi(1, 1) = \frac{\binom{9}{1}\binom{1}{1}}{\binom{10}{2}} \qquad \pi(1, 2) = 0$$

$$\pi(i, y) = \frac{\binom{i}{y}\binom{10-i}{2-y}}{\binom{10}{2}} \qquad \begin{array}{l} i = 2, 3, \ldots, 8 \\ y = 0, 1, 2 \end{array}$$

$$\pi(9, 0) = 0 \qquad \pi(9, 1) = \frac{\binom{1}{1}\binom{9}{1}}{\binom{10}{2}} \qquad \pi(9, 2) = \frac{\binom{9}{2}}{\binom{10}{2}}$$

$$\pi(10, 0) = 0 \qquad \pi(10, 1) = 0 \qquad \pi(10, 2) = 1 \qquad (4\text{-}4\text{-}9)$$

From these expressions it is possible to compute:

$$P\{X_2 \le k \mid e_i\} = \sum_{y=0}^{k} \pi(i, y) \qquad (4\text{-}4\text{-}10)$$

given in Figure 4-4-6.

From relations (4-4-7) and (4-4-8) we obtain that:

$$\begin{aligned} w(e_i, \delta^{(k)}) &= q(e_i, d_0) P\{X_2 \le k \mid e_i\} + q(e_i, d_1) \cdot P\{X_2 > k \mid e_i\} \\ &= (q(e_i, d_0) - q(e_i, d_1)) P\{X_2 \le k \mid e_i\} + q(e_i, d_1) \quad (4\text{-}4\text{-}10) \end{aligned}$$

which is evaluated in Figure 4-4-7. From that table we can obtain that the maximum of this opportunity loss function for each decision rule $\delta^{(k)}$, $k = 0, 1, 2$, is given by $t(\delta^{(0)}) = \$105/45$, $t(\delta^{(1)}) = \$350/45$, and $t(\delta^{(2)}) = \$10$. Using the minimax opportunity loss criteria, we determine that $\delta^{(0)}$

i \ y	$P\{X_2 \le k \mid e_i\}$ 0	1	2
0	1	1	1
1	36/45	1	1
2	28/45	44/45	1
3	21/45	42/45	1
4	15/45	39/45	1
5	10/45	35/45	1
6	6/45	30/45	1
7	3/45	24/45	1
8	1/45	17/45	1
9	0	9/45	1
10	0	0	1

FIGURE 4-4-6. Cumulative hypergeometric probabilities

is the best decision rule. (This rule is selected as the best rule before actually performing the sampling.) To apply the rule, the boy must call two potential customers and note the number of affirmative replies to his question concerning their desire to buy a Christmas tree. If none of the people reply affirmatively, he will not buy the trees. But if at least one person replies affirmatively, he will purchase 5 trees.

Event	$\delta^{(0)}$	$\delta^{(1)}$	$\delta^{(2)}$
e_0	\$0	\$0	\$0
e_1	\$18/45	\$0	\$0
e_2	\$28/45	\$44/45	\$1
e_3	\$84/45	\$168/45	\$4
e_4	\$105/45	\$273/45	\$7
e_5	\$100/45	\$350/45	\$10
e_6	\$60/45	\$300/45	\$10
e_7	\$30/45	\$240/45	\$10
e_8	\$10/45	\$170/45	\$10
e_9	\$0	\$90/45	\$10
e_{10}	\$0	\$0	\$10

FIGURE 4-4-7. Conditional expected opportunity loss function for problem 4-4-1

In general, there are many ways to define decision rules which will determine a decision $d_j\, j = 0, 1, \ldots J$ for every possible outcome of the sample. As we saw in the last example, one of the possible decisions, d_0, may be to do nothing, and it is usually desirable to include such a possibility. A difficult problem which may be encountered, in applying the methods of this section, is the evaluation of $P\{\delta^{(k)} = d_j | e_i\}$ for all possible event-decision combinations. This is necessary in the evaluation of the conditional expected opportunity loss function,

$$w(e_i, \delta^{(k)}) = \sum_{j=0}^{J} q(e_i, d_j)P\{\delta^{(k)} = d_j | e_i\} \qquad (4\text{-}4\text{-}11)$$

upon which the selection of the best decision rule is based. Although our examples only cover two possible decisions, the reasoning is analogous for more than two.

4–5. DECISION MAKING—PRIOR PROBABILITIES—SAMPLING

The starting point for the introduction of prior probabilities into the procedure for selecting the best decision rule will be the expected opportunity loss function $w(e_i, \delta^{(k)})$. If we consider this function as an opportunity loss function, with the decision rules playing the role that decisions d_j played in Section 4-3, then the reasoning of Section 4-3 may be used. We form the function $v(\delta^{(k)}) = \sum_{i=1}^{I} p_i \, w(e_i, \delta^{(k)})$, and choose as the best decision rule the one which minimizes $v(\delta^{(k)})$. The function $v(\delta^{(k)})$ can be interpreted as the *expected* expected conditional opportunity loss if decision rule $\delta^{(k)}$ is used. Therefore, the best decision rule is the one that minimizes the *expected* expected conditional opportunity loss.

If we consider the function $w(e_i, \delta^{(k)})$ (see Figure 4-4-7) and the prior probability distribution given in Figure 4-5-1, we may compute the *expected* expected opportunity loss function to be $v(\delta^{(0)}) = \$\frac{576}{450}$, $v(\delta^{(1)}) = \$\frac{1692}{450}$, and $v(\delta^{(1)}) = \$\frac{2250}{450}$, from which it follows that $\delta^{(0)}$ is the best decision rule. An examination of Figure 4-4-7 would show that only if the event e_1 occurs will $\delta^{(1)}$ or $\delta^{(2)}$ be superior to $\delta^{(0)}$. Therefore, the decision rules $\delta^{(1)}$ or $\delta^{(2)}$ would only be selected as the best rules if the prior probability of e_1 was very large.

Events	e_0	e_1	e_2	e_3	e_4	e_5	e_6	e_7	e_8	e_9	e_{10}
Prior probabilities	0	.2	.2	.1	.2	.1	.1	.1	0	0	0

FIGURE 4-5-1. Prior probability distribution for problem 4-4-1

Let us now try to determine what we have gained by sampling. If we consider the prior probabilities of Figure 4-5-1 and the opportunity loss function of Figure 4-4-5, we can determine, by the methods of Section 4-3, what the best decision would be without sampling. We first compute the expected opportunity loss function to be $v(d_0) = \$5$ and $v(d_1) = \$.40$, and make the decision which minimizes the expected opportunity loss: decision d_1, buy the 5 Christmas trees. Our average opportunity loss will be $\$.40$. On the other hand, if we allow the possibility of taking a sample of size 2 and use the best decision rule $\delta^{(0)}$, we will suffer an average opportunity loss of $\$\frac{576}{450}$. By sampling, therefore, we have actually increased our expected opportunity loss, which implies that it is better, in this case, not to take a sample of size 2 than it is to take one. Before drawing a sample, it is important to determine whether or not sampling actually decreases the expected opportunity loss; it may not. One reason for an increase in the expected opportunity loss is that the sample information is not used effectively. Although we selected the best decision rule of the three being considered, there are other possible decision rules which could give smaller *expected* expected opportunity losses than that given by $\delta^{(0)}$. If no decision rule can be found which gives a smaller *expected* expected opportunity loss than the smallest without sampling, then sampling should not be performed.

Another reason why one may not wish to sample is that the cost of sampling might be more than the amount that could be saved by obtaining the additional information. Until now, we have not considered sampling costs, but let us assume that, in Problem 4-4-1, it would cost $\$.10$ for each phone call. If the boy decides to call all 10 potential customers, he will be able to determine the exact number of trees that he will sell. Without going through a formal definition of a decision rule, it is intuitively clear that, with this information, his minimum *expected* expected opportunity loss will be zero. He will, however, spend $1 for the telephone calls, which will be the cost of sampling. We will define the total loss for a sample of size N to be the sum of the minimum *expected* expected opportunity loss plus the cost of sampling. (The minimum *expected* expected opportunity loss depends upon the set of decision rules being considered and may not be the smallest possible *expected* expected opportunity loss if every possible decision rule were considered.) Thus, the total loss for a sample of size 10 is $1, whereas the total loss for a sample of size 2 is $\$\frac{576}{450} + \$.20 = \$\frac{666}{450}$, indicating that a sample of size 10 is better than a sample of size 2. The total loss for a sample of size 0 will be defined as the minimum expected opportunity which, in this case, is $\$.40$. Whether or not it is profitable to sample will be decided, based on the total loss from a sample. If the total loss from a sample of size 0 is the minimum of the total loss function, then no sampling should be performed. On the other hand, if the minimum of the total loss function is obtained for a sample size n^*, then sampling should be performed, and the size of the sample should be n^*.

Once the sample size has been decided upon, it is then possible to refer back to the calculations to determine the best decision rule for that sample. If we decide, in the previous example, that a sample size of 2 is the best (although our calculations indicated that it is not), then the best decision rule would be $\delta^{(0)}$. The sample is then selected and, based upon the outcome of the sample, a final decision is made using this decision rule. Thus, if we take the sample of size 2, and we receive one affirmative answer, the decision rule $\delta^{(0)}$ gives us decision d_1, purchase 5 Christmas trees.

We have only discussed the very simplest type of decision rules requiring that one of the final decisions d_j, corresponding to some action, be made after the sample is drawn. More general rules allow for the possibility of deciding to draw another sample, as a result of the first sample, rather than making any of the final decisions. These are called *sequential decision rules*, and one of their advantages is that they could decrease the cost of sampling and, therefore, decrease the total loss. Taking a sample of size 2 and using rule $\delta^{(0)}$, if the first phone call brings an affirmative response, the boy would make decision d_1—no matter what the outcome of the second call. In order to strictly apply rule $\delta^{(0)}$, it is necessary to make two calls. A sequential decision rule that accomplished the same final results as $\delta^{(0)}$ might be stated: Make the first phone call; if the answer is affirmative, make decision d_1. Otherwise, make a second call; if that answer is affirmative, make decision d_1. If not, make decision d_0. So, if the first call is affirmative, the second call is not made (meaning a smaller sample size, on the average).

Another advantage in using sequential decision rules is that, in some cases, the observations are naturally obtained in a sequential order. In Problem 1-1-1, the weekly demands are available at the end of each week. Based upon these observations, any decision rule which is sequential would allow the possibility of a decision sooner than if we must wait until a certain number of observations are available before making a final decision This type of decision rule has had much application in the area of statistical quality control. The analysis of the expected losses involved, when using sequential decision rules, requires more complicated probabilistic arguments. But the general concept of evaluating various rules by comparing the total expected loss is still valid. The total loss is now composed of the *expected* expected opportunity loss and the expected cost of sampling, since the size of the sample is now a random variable. This last fact introduces more complication into the evaluation of the performance of various rules. Although a sequential decision rule does not require the selection of a sample size prior to sampling, before the sequential rule is applied it is still necessary to determine if no sampling would yield a smaller total loss than any other of the available sequential decision rules.

Exercises

4-1. A candy store owner must decide how many large, expensive chocolate rabbits to stock for the Easter season. One rabbit costs $4 and sells for $7.50. Any rabbits not sold by Easter can be sold afterward at 30 per cent below cost. From past experience the owner knows that the demand for these rabbits never exceeds 4. Compute the payoff table and the opportunity loss table. Using the maximin payoff criteria what is the best decision? Using the minimax oppoutunity loss criteria?

4-2. A newsstand dealer buys the *Daily Racing Form* for 30 cents per copy and sells it at 50 cents. Any copies remaining unsold, after the race, are valueless. If the only possible events are that from 21 to 26 copies are sold, and if the possible decisions are that from 21 to 26 copies will be stocked, compute the payoff table and the opportunity loss table. What is the best decision using the maximin payoff criteria? Using the minimax opportunity loss criteria?

4-3. If, in Exercise 4-1, the store owner has the prior distribution:

number demanded	0	1	2	3	4
prior probability	.1	.2	.3	.3	.1

then determine the best decision using the maximum expected payoff criteria.

4-4. If, in Exercise 4-2, the newsstand dealer has the prior distribution:

number demanded	21	22	23	24	25	26
prior probability	.10	.15	.20	.30	.14	.11

then determine the best decision using the minimum expected opportunity loss criteria.

4-5. A man is offered the opportunity to invest $10,000 in a wildcat operation in Texas. If the well produces an average of 3,001 to 5,000 barrels per day for a year, he will be paid $100,000. If it produces 1,500 to 3,000 barrels, he will be paid $50,000; and if it produces less than 1,500 barrels, he will receive nothing. There is no chance that the well will produce an average of more than 5,000 barrels per day. If he does not invest in the well he will be assured of $500.00. He estimates that an average production of less than 1,500 barrels per day will have probability 0.6; and average production of 1,500 to 3,000 barrels will have probability 0.3; and 3,001 to 5,000 will have probability 0.1. Should he invest in this venture?

4–6. A manufacturer of bearings is faced with the decision of accepting a lot of 1,000 bearings or rejecting it. From prior considerations, he knows that the machine can be set in such a way that it will produce defectives with probability $p = .02$ or $p = .10$. If the event that defectives will be produced with $p = .02$ is called e_1, and the event that defectives will be produced with $p = .10$ is e_2, then we can write the payoff table for this problem as:

Decisions

Event	d_1 (accept)	d_2 (reject)
e_1	0	$-\$200$
e_2	$-\$100$	$-\$50$

If the manufacturer takes a sample of size 3, observes the number of defectives (X), and uses the decision rule $\delta^{(C)}$: *Reject if $X > C$; accept if $X \leq C$; $C = 0, 1, 2, 3$,* then what is the best value of C to use in the decision rule? (Assume that X is a binomial random variable in making the necessary calculations.)

4–7. If we assume, in Exercise 4–6, that the prior probabilities of events e_1 and e_2 are .6 and .4, respectively, then what is the best value of C to use in the decision rule?

4–8. If we assume, in Exercise 4–7, that the cost of sampling is 50 cents per item, with a fixed cost of $2, should the manufacture take a sample?

4–9. A publisher is trying to decide whether to publish a manuscript he has received. In making a decision, he feels that it is sufficient to imagine four possible events: e_1: 1500 sold; e_2: 2500 copies sold; e_3: 3500 copies sold; e_4: 10,000 copies sold. The prior probabilities assigned to these events are: $p(e_1) = 0.30$, $p(e_2) = 0.40$, $p(e_3) = 0.25$, and $p(e_4) = 0.05$. If he publishes the book, the discounted profits for each event are: $-\$30,000$ for e_1; $\$4,000$ for e_2; $\$12,000$ for e_3, and $\$100,000$ for e_4. If he does not publish, the discounted profit is 0. To gain additional information, he sends the book to two reviewers, and he will use the decision rule: Publish if j reviews are favorable; otherwise, do not publish, $j = 0, 1, 2$. From previous experience he knows that each reviewer acts independently and the conditional probabilities of a favorable review, given each event, is $0.10, 0.30, 0.50$, and 0.10, for the type of manuscript under consideration. If he receives one favorable review and one unfavorable review, should he publish the manuscript?

4–10. In the previous exercise, if the publisher thinks that the prior probability distribution for events e_1 through e_4 is: $p(e_1) = .4$, $p(e_2) = .3, p(e_3) = .2$, and $p(e_4) = .1$, should he publish if he receives one favorable review and one unfavorable review?

4–11. If, in Exercise 4–10 the cost of reviewing a book is \$250 per review, does it pay to send the book out for review?

4–12. For Problem 3-2-1, assume that the prior distribution for the events e_i is $p(e_0) = .1, p(e_1) = .4, p(e_2) = .3, p(e_3) = .1$, and $p(e_4) = .1$. Use the reasoning of Section 4-5 to determine which decision rule is best.

4–13. For the critical regions given in Exercise 3–5, define corresponding decision rules. Use the reasoning of Section 4-4 to determine the best decision rule. Assuming the same prior probability distribution given in Exercise 4–12, determine the best decision rule by the reasoning of Section 4-5.

Further Reading

Bierman, H., *et al.*, *Quantitative Analysis for Business Decisions*, rev. ed. Homewood, Ill.: Richard D. Irwin, Inc., 1965.

Bryant, E. C., *Statistical Analysis*, second ed. New York: McGraw-Hill Book Company, 1966.

Chernoff, H., and L. E. Moses, *Elementary Decision Theory*. New York: John Wiley & Sons, Inc., 1959.

Dixon, W., and F. J. Massey, Jr., *Introduction to Statistical Analysis*, second ed. New York: McGraw-Hill Book Company, 1957.

Ehrenfeld, S., and S. Littauer, *Introduction to Statistical Method*. New York: McGraw-Hill Book Company, 1964.

Fisher, R. A., *Statistical Methods and Scientific Inference*. New York: Hafner Publishing Co., Inc., 1959.

Griffin, J. L., *Statistics: Methods and Application*. New York: Holt, Rinehart & Winston, Inc., 1962.

Hadley, G., *Introduction to Probability and Statistical Decision Theory*. San Francisco: Holden-Day, Inc., 1967.

Hoel, P. G., *Introduction to Mathematical Statistics*, third ed. New York: John Wiley & Sons, Inc., 1962.

Mood, A. M., and F. A. Graybill, *Introduction to the Theory of Statistics*, second ed. New York: McGraw-Hill Book Company, 1963.

Neyman, J., *First Course in Probability and Statistics*. New York: Holt, Rinehart & Winston, Inc., 1950.

Peters, W. S., and G. W. Summers, *Statistical Analysis for Business Decisions*. Englewood Cliffs, N. J.: Prentice-Hall, Inc., 1968.

Savage, L. J., *The Foundations of Statistics*. New York: John Wiley & Sons, Inc., 1957.

Schlaifer, R., *Probability and Statistics for Business Decisions*. New York: McGraw-Hill Book Company, 1959.

Siegel, S., *Non-Paremetric Statistics*. New York: McGraw-Hill Book Company, 1956.

Wallis, W. A., and H. V. Roberts, *Statistics—A New Approach*. Glencoe, Ill.: The Free Press, 1956.

Weiss, L., *Statistical Decision Theory*. New York: McGraw-Hill Book Company, 1961.

Williams, E. J., *Regression Analysis*. New York: John Wiley & Sons, Inc., 1959.

Index